Physical Science 8
Student Guide

Part 1

Printed by Courier, Kendallville, IN, USA, April 2014, Lot 042014

Table of Contents

Unit 4: Force and Motion

Unit 5: Semester 1 Assessment

Student Guide
Lesson 1: Introduction to Physical Science

What do you see around you? Probably your computer, a lamp, a desk, and a chair. How can you describe them? What are they made of? For about 200 years, we have known that all matter is made of atoms. That means that the computer, lamp, desk, and chair are made of atoms. In order to determine what atoms are made of, scientists do experiments. From the experiments, scientists construct descriptions, or models, of what atoms are like and use the models to predict the behavior of atoms. You will explore all that and more in this unit.

Lesson Objectives

- Describe physical science as the study of matter and energy.

PREPARE

Approximate lesson time is 60 minutes.

Materials

For the Student

🖥 Keeping a Science Notebook

LEARN
Activity 1: Introduction to Physical Science (Online)

Activity 2: Keeping a Science Notebook (Online)

Name _____ Date _____

Keeping a Science Notebook

As you go through the course, you should maintain a Science Notebook. Here is a suggested way to go about keeping good, easy-to-find notes. The following are the main sections of a good Science Notebook:

- Lesson Title

- Notes

- Activity (or Lab) Title

- Procedures

- Data

- Analysis

- Conclusion

Be aware that you may not need every section for every lesson. Let's examine each section in detail.

Lesson Title: It would be a good idea at the beginning of every lesson to write the title of the lesson you will be reviewing. For easy reference, note which unit the lesson belongs to.

Notes: You will read and learn (and review) a lot of content this year. Writing good notes is a skill that requires practice. Doing so will help you recognize what concepts are important on any given screen and what details help support those main concepts.

Activity (or Lab) Title: This is, of course, where the title of the activity or lab goes. In the case of a lab lesson, the lab title is the same as the lesson title. Writing the title will help you focus on the main topic of the activity and will provide an easy reference for later review.

Procedures: Each lab will list precisely what procedures should be followed. In your Science Notebook, you don't need to rewrite the entire list of procedures. Rather, this section should have a basic overview of what you did in the lab and should serve as a reminder about how the lab was performed.

Data: In this section, you will write observations, make data tables and calculations, and so forth. When you write observations, try to be as specific as possible. For example, don't simply write, "When heated, the solution bubbled." Write, "When the solution was heated, small white bubbles (about 2 to 3 mm in size) formed on the surface of the liquid." Many tables and graphs will be given to you in PDF form in the activity. You do not need to redo these tables and charts in your Science Notebook; simply put in a reference to the worksheet in your Science Notebook so you will know where to find the information if you need it later.

Analysis: In this section, you will make any calculations necessary and write down your ideas about what they mean. You might also be asked questions in this section. If there is room provided on the worksheet for the answers, then you don't have to recopy them into your Science Notebook. If there is not room on the worksheet, though, you should answer the questions in this section of your notebook. You should also write down any problems that occurred during the activity, as well as possible solutions to them.

Conclusion: Many of the labs will have an Analysis or Conclusion section, where you will be asked to form a conclusion about the lab and asked questions about what you can infer from the lab. In your Science Notebook, you should be sure to write any general conclusions you can make about the lab. Since every question you answer in science usually leads to more questions, you should also write any new questions you have that result from the lab. Now that we have discussed what information should be included in your Science Notebook, let's look at a page in an upcoming lesson.

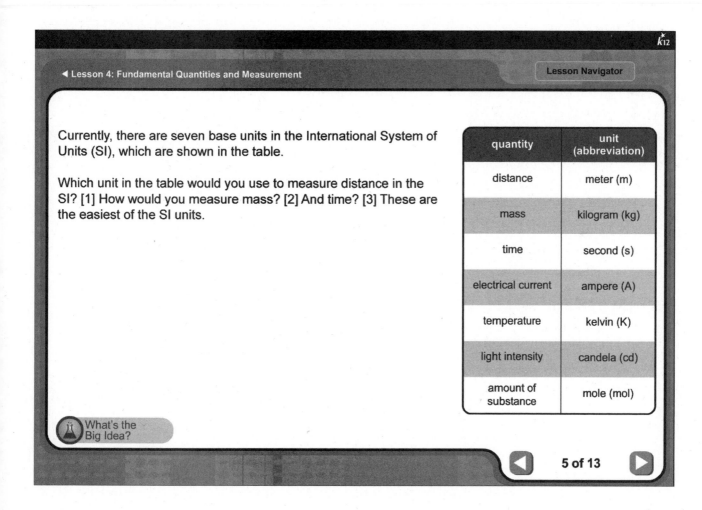

◄ Lesson 4: Fundamental Quantities and Measurement

Lesson Navigator

Currently, there are seven base units in the International System of Units (SI), which are shown in the table.

Which unit in the table would you use to measure distance in the SI? [1] How would you measure mass? [2] And time? [3] These are the easiest of the SI units.

quantity	unit (abbreviation)
distance	meter (m)
mass	kilogram (kg)
time	second (s)
electrical current	ampere (A)
temperature	kelvin (K)
light intensity	candela (cd)
amount of substance	mole (mol)

What's the Big Idea?

5 of 13

Questions

1. What's the title of this lesson? Write this in your Science Notebook.

   _____

   _____

   _____

   _____

   _____

   _____

   _____

   _____

2. As you began reading through the content, you would start taking notes. What are the important concepts on this page? Take a moment to write what you think the important concepts are and compare your ideas with the activity answer key.

   _____

   _____

   _____

   _____

   _____

   _____

   _____

   _____

3. Now write the title for this activity and the procedures. Data and conclusions don't directly apply, but fill them in as best you can, then compare your Science Notebook with the activity answer key.

   _____

   _____

   _____

   _____

   _____

   _____

   _____

   _____

Student Guide
Lesson 2: Physical Systems

Lesson Objectives

- Distinguish between a closed system and an open system.
- Describe how scientists use models to represent and predict real phenomena in the physical world.
- Define universal law and give an example.
- Recognize that models change to accommodate new discoveries and observations.

PREPARE

Approximate lesson time is 60 minutes.

Materials

For the Student

- 💻 Physical Systems Review
- 💻 The Aquarium System

Keywords and Pronunciation

theory : a scientific explanation that accounts for observations of many types.

universal law : a principle that is in effect always and everywhere

---

LEARN
Activity 1: Physical Systems (Online)

Activity 2: Physical Systems (Online)

Activity 3: The Aquarium System (Online)

ASSESS

Lesson Assessment: Physical Systems (Online)

You will complete an online assessment covering the main objectives of this lesson. Your assessment will be scored by the computer.

Name _____   Date _____

Physical Systems Review

Review what you have learned about physical systems. When finished, place your completed lesson review sheet in your Science Notebook.

Vocabulary Review

Read each definition. Match each term in the Word Bank with its definition. Write the letter of the correct answer on the blank in front of the definition.

<u>Word Bank</u>

A. model

B. system

C. open system

D. closed system

E. universal law

1. _____ a type of system in which something coming in from the outside or something leaving the system affects the system

2. _____ a principle that is in effect everywhere at all times

3. _____ a group of things that interact with one another

4. _____ a type of system in which nothing goes in or out that affects the system

5. _____ a representation of a real system or process that helps you understand the actual system or process

Short Answer

Read the information below. Write your answer after the question.

6. The model of the atom has changed dramatically over time. What factors account for these changes in the atomic model?

_____

_____

_____

_____

Name   Date

The Aquarium System

Introduction

A *closed system* is one in which nothing goes in or out of the system that affects its observed condition or the behavior being studied. An *open system* is one in which something coming in from the outside or something leaving the system affects it. In this activity, put your understanding of these concepts to the test.

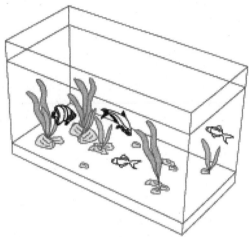

Figure 1

Procedure

At first glance, the aquarium in **Figure 1**, with its contents, may look like a closed system. Look carefully at the organisms and the structure of the tank.

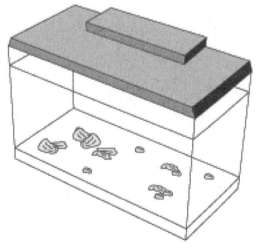

Figure 2

Now consider the same tank (**Figure 2**) with all organisms removed. All that is left are the water and the rocks. There is also a top that seals the aquarium tank so no water or air can get out or in.

Analysis and Conclusion

1. In what respects can the aquarium in Figure 1 be considered an open system?

    _____

    _____

    _____

    _____

2. In what way could the aquarium in Figure 2 be considered a closed system? Why?

    _____

    _____

    _____

3. In what respects could the aquarium in Figure 2 still be considered an open system? Why?

    _____

    _____

4. Think of your answer for Question 3. What would you need to do to make it a closed system?

    _____

    _____

    _____

    _____

    _____

    _____

Student Guide
Lesson 3: Measurement and the International System

Lesson Objectives

- Explain why scientists need a system of measurements.
- Measure physical quantities using the International System of Units (SI).
- Identify fundamental units of the SI and associate each unit with what it measures.

PREPARE

Approximate lesson time is 60 minutes.

Materials

For the Student

- 🖳 Measurement and SI Review
- 🖳 Show Me the Money (and I'll measure it)!

  dime

  nickel

  quarter

  ruler (metric & customary)

  paper

  pencil

  penny

  scissors

Keywords and Pronunciation

ampere : a unit of electical current flow

candela (kan-DEE-luh) : an SI unit of luminosity

kelvin : an SI unit of temperature

kilogram : an SI unit of mass

meter : an SI unit of length

model : an artificial representation of a real system or process, designed to help understand the structure or behavior of the actual system or process

mole : an SI unit of the amount of a substance

second : an SI unit of time

SI : SI, le Système International d´Unités (international system of units), specifies the metric system of physical quantities

spectroscope

theory : a scientific explanation that accounts for observations of many types.

universal law : a principle that is in effect always and everywhere

LEARN
Activity 1: Measurement and the International System *(Online)*

Activity 2: Measurement and the International System *(Online)*

Activity 3: Show Me the Money (and I'll measure it)! *(Online)*

ASSESS

Lesson Assessment: Measurement and the International System (*Online*)

You will complete an online assessment covering the main objectives of this lesson. Your assessment will be scored by the computer.

Name _____   Date _____

Measurement and the International System Review

Choose the SI unit from the list that would give the best measurement for each of the situations below.

SI Measurements

- second
- ampere
- kilogram
- meter
- mole
- Kelvin
- candela

Situations

1. the length of a field   _____

2. the mass of a baby   _____

3. the brightness of a lightbulb   _____

4. the amount of a substance   _____

5. the temperature of a liquid   _____

6. the time that has elapsed   _____

7. the amount of electrical current necessary to light a lightbulb   _____

Name _____   Date _____

Show Me the Money (and I'll measure it)!

Materials
ruler with cm and mm markings
plain piece of paper
scissors
sharp pencil
copy of the attached table
penny
nickel
dime
quarter

Procedures – Part A

1. Cut out three strips of paper, each 10 cm long and approximately 3 cm wide (the width is not as important).

2. Make a "copied mm ruler" by using the actual ruler to mark one of the paper strips every mm for 10 cm. Label every 10 mm.

3. Make your own "copied cm ruler" by using the actual ruler to mark one of the paper strips every centimeter for 10 cm (do not mark the millimeter divisions). Label every 1 cm.

4. Make your own "handmade mm ruler" by using the actual ruler to mark one of the paper strips every 5 mm for 10 cm (do not mark the millimeter divisions). Label every 1 cm. Using only your eye to estimate the distances, mark off the millimeter divisions on this ruler.

5. There should now be a total of four rulers, three paper rulers and one real ruler.

6. Using each of your rulers and the real ruler, measure the thickness and diameter of each of the coins. Record the measured values in Data Table 1. Be sure to report the measurements using the appropriate number of significant figures.

7. The actual dimensions provided by the U.S. Mint are given in the last row.

Data Table 1

	Penny Thickness	Penny Diameter	Nickel Thickness	Nickel Diameter	Dime Thickness	Dime Diameter	Quarter Thickness	Quarter Diameter
Copied cm ruler								
Handmade mm ruler								
Copied mm ruler								
Real ruler (mm)								
U.S. Mint website	1.55 mm	19.05 mm	1.95 mm	21.21 mm	1.35 mm	17.91 mm	1.75 mm	24.26 mm

Analysis and Conclusion

1. List the rulers, including the original reference ruler, in order from the one that resulted in the most accurate measurements to the one that resulted in the least accurate measurements.

    _____

    _____

    _____

    _____

2. Explain why you listed the rulers in the order that you did.

    _____

    _____

    _____

    _____

3. List the rulers, including the original reference ruler, in order from the one that resulted in the most precise measurements to the one that resulted in the least precise measurements.

_____

_____

_____

_____

4. Is there a difference between your measured values and those provided by the U.S. Mint? Why would this be?

_____

_____

_____

_____

Student Guide
Lesson 4: LAB: Measured Steps

Lesson Objectives

- Measure and record data about physical objects.
- Design an appropriate format to collect measurement data and to record the results of calculations.
- Draw conclusions based on the data recorded.

PREPARE

Approximate lesson time is 60 minutes.

Materials

For the Student

📖 Measuring and Recording Measurements

📖 Speed

meter stick

stopwatch

household items

ruler, metric

scissors

string

LEARN
Activity 1: Measured Steps *(Online)*

Name _____   Date _____

Measured Steps Activity 1 – Measuring and Recording Measurements

Materials

- string
- scissors
- meter stick (with centimeter markings)
- ruler (with millimeter markings)
- various household objects – table, chair, book, pencil

Introduction

In these exercises, you will be making measurements. The objective is not to get right answers, but to understand how you can measure using different methods and to understand what kinds of results you might get by using different methods of measurement. When you make a measurement, make it independently of any other measurement. If you get one result from measuring something one way, do not think about that measurement when you measure the same thing another way or another time. Obtain the result from each measurement separately. If you get similar results, it should be because your measurements turn out that way, not because you decided they should be similar. (If possible, have one or more assistants make some of the repeated measurements, but do not share your results until all the measurements have been done. If you do this, decide whether your helpers should use your hand or their own for their measurement using a real hand.)

Procedures

1. Stretch a piece of string so that it runs from the base of your palm to the tip of your longest finger.

2. Cut this length of string. Since it is the length of your hand, you will use it as one tool to measure objects in hands.

3. Select five common household objects of various sizes or areas around your home to measure (for example, a room, a table, a chair, a book, and a pencil).

4. Using your hand, measure the width of each object to determine how many hands wide it is. Record this measurement in the Methods of Measuring Data Table.

5. Using the "hand" string, measure each object to determine how many hands wide it is (don't use the first measurement you made with your hand to anticipate the answer). Record this measurement.

6. Using the meter stick, measure each object to determine how many meters wide it is. Record this measurement.

7. Using the metric side of the ruler, measure each object to determine how many centimeters wide it is. Record this measurement.

8. Repeat Steps 4 through 7 two more times so you have three measurements of each type for each item. Remember to make these measurements independently from one another, as suggested in the introduction.

Methods of Measuring Data Table

Object	Hand			"Hand" String			Meter Stick (m)			Metric Ruler (cm)		
	Trials			Trials			Trials			Trials		
	1	2	3	1	2	3	1	2	3	1	2	3
1.												
2.												
3.												
4.												
5.												

Analysis

1. Which measuring device was the most challenging to use to obtain a measurement that would help someone else know the sizes of the objects you measured? Explain your answer, including as many reasons as you can think of.

2. Which measuring device was the most effective for measuring very large objects, such as the room? Why?

3. Which measuring device was the most effective for measuring very small objects, such as the pencil? Why?

4. If other students completed the same experiment using the same objects you used, but using their own hand, how would the measurements compare with yours?

5. How do you think those students' measurements using the metric stick and the ruler would compare with yours?

Name _____ Date _____

Measured Steps Activity 2 – Speed

Goal

The goal of this activity is to calculate a quantity that is derived from other, more basic, quantities that are measured.

Materials

- meter stick
- stopwatch

Procedures for Exercise A

1. Find a long, open area, either inside or outside, where you can move easily. If possible, a space the length of a couple of rooms would be good, and it could be as long as half a block. If you must work indoors, find the longest space you can. You will cross this area by running, hopping, and walking slowly, so make sure no large obstacles are in the way. (Be careful when you run.)

2. Using the meter stick, measure the length of the open area that you selected. Record this measurement in the Speed Data Table under column 1, labeled Distance Traveled. Record the same distance for each of the three trials because you will use the same space.

3. You will time yourself as you cross the area, using two different methods: a stopwatch and hand clapping. You will record your results in the Travel Time Data Table.

4. For your first trial, run across the space. Start the stopwatch when you begin. As you run across the space, you will also clap your hands. Count the number of claps you make as one method to measure time. When you reach the other side of the area, stop the stopwatch. Record the time and the number of claps in the Travel Time Data Table. *Hint:* If you have difficulty working your stopwatch and clapping at the same time, run across the space two times, once using the stopwatch and once clapping. It will be easier to perform this activity if you have a friend or parent to time you with the stopwatch.

5. Reset the stopwatch to zero, then repeat Step 4, this time hopping across the space while clapping your hands. Record the data in the Travel Time Data Table.

6. Repeat Step 4, this time walking slowly while clapping. Record the data in the Travel Time Data Table.

7. Repeat Steps 4, 5, and 6 two more times, so that you have a total of three trials of each movement type.

Name _____   Date _____

Model Problems Assessment

Questions 1–4 are online. As you think about the following question, keep in mind the various methods scientists use to solve problems. What methods would you use to collect and record data?

(10 pts.)

1. Alecia is investigating two rock samples that glow in a darkened room. What can she do to compare these samples and report on her findings?

Student Guide
Lesson 8: Unit Review

Lesson Objectives

- Describe and explain a model system physicists have used to represent a real phenomenon.
- Make measurements using the SI system.
- Differentiate different samples using factors such as density, size, and temperature.

PREPARE

Approximate lesson time is 60 minutes.

Keywords and Pronunciation

ampere : a unit of electical current flow

candela (kan-DEE-luh) : an SI unit of luminosity

kelvin : an SI unit of temperature

kilogram : an SI unit of mass

meter : an SI unit of length

model : an artificial representation of a real system or process, designed to help understand the structure or behavior of the actual system or process

mole : an SI unit of the amount of a substance

second : an SI unit of time

LEARN
Activity 1: Unit Review *(Online)*

Student Guide
Lesson 9: Unit Assessment

Lesson Objectives

- Describe and explain a model system physicists have used to represent a real phenomenon.
- Describe physical science as the study of matter and energy.
- Make measurements using the SI system.
- Differentiate different samples using factors such as density, size, and temperature.

PREPARE

Approximate lesson time is 60 minutes.

ASSESS

Unit Assessment: Introduction to Physical Science, Part 1 (*Online*)

You will complete an online assessment of the main objectives covered so far in this unit. Follow the instructions online. Your assessment will be scored by the computer.

Unit Assessment: Introduction to Physical Science, Part 2 (*Offline*)

Complete the offline part of the Unit Assessment. Your learning coach will score this part of the Assessment.

Student Guide
Lesson 1: Atoms

What do you know about a melting ice cube? It is cold, hard, the water is wet, and perhaps a few other things. What scientists have learned about ice and water could fill books. The ice and water are made of very small particles, called molecules, which are made of still smaller particles, called atoms.

In this unit on Matter, you will learn about the scientific discoveries that explain the nature of the materials that make up your world. You will also learn how and why these materials change.

Lesson Objectives

- Explain that all matter is made up of atoms.
- Describe one model structure of an atom as a nucleus made up of protons and neutrons, surrounded by electrons.
- Describe how and why models of the atom have changed over time.

PREPARE

Approximate lesson time is 60 minutes.

Advance Preparation

- If you don't already have it, please gather sesame seeds, poppy seeds, fiberfill (cotton or synthetic), forceps (tweezers), permanent marker, and rubber cement for the Build an Atom Model activity.

Materials

For the Student

    🖳 Build an Atom Model

    tweezers

    marker, permanent

    rubber cement

    ruler, metric

    seeds, poppy

    seeds, sesame

    stuffing

Keywords and Pronunciation

atom : A tiny particle that is the fundamental building block of substances. The properties of the atom determine the properties of the element made up only of those atoms.

electron : a negatively charged particle with much less mass than protons and neutrons (approximately 1/2000), found around the nuclei of atoms

element : a type of atom, with a particular number of protons in the nucleus; a pure substance with only one type of atom throughout

neutron : a neutral particle with approximately the same mass as a proton, found in nuclei of atoms along with protons

LEARN
Activity 1: Atoms (Online)

Activity 2: Build an Atom Model (Online)

ASSESS
Lesson Assessment: Atoms, Part 1 (Online)

You will complete an online assessment covering the main objectives of this lesson. Your assessment will be scored by the computer.

Lesson Assessment: Atoms, Part 2 (Offline)

You will complete an offline assessment covering the main objectives of this lesson. Your learning coach will score this assessment.

Name _____   Date _____

Build an Atom Model

Materials

- cm ruler
- sesame seeds
- poppy seeds
- fiberfill (cotton or synthetic stuffing)
- forceps (tweezers)
- permanent marker
- rubber cement

Procedures

1. You will build a model of a helium-4 atom, which contains 2 neutrons and 2 protons in the nucleus, along with 2 electrons outside the nucleus.

2. Begin by coloring 2 sesame seeds with the permanent marker. These colored seeds represent neutrons.

3. Using rubber cement, attach the 2 colored sesame seeds to 2 plain sesame seeds. This will be the model of the helium-4 nucleus. Let it dry for a few minutes.

4. Make a ball of fiberfill that is approximately 10 cm in diameter.

5. Insert the 4-sesame-seed nucleus into the middle of the fiberfill puff. Glue 2 poppy seed electrons to the outside of the fiberfill at different locations.

Something to Think About

For a larger, more realistic model, put 4 sesame seeds (2 colored and 2 plain) in the center of a large room in your house. Place 1 poppy seed in an adjacent room and place another poppy seed in another adjacent room. How did your perspective on the amount of space involved in an atomic model change? Note: For a correct relative scale, you would place 2 poppy seeds one block away, each in a different place, and 2 poppy seeds 2 blocks away, each in a different place.

Optional Activity

1. If you have time, make a 3-D model of the neon-20 atom. To model the nucleus you will need 10 colored sesame seeds (neutrons) and 10 plain sesame seeds (protons). Glue all the sesame seeds together.

2. Make a larger puff of cotton for the outer electrons in the model than you made for the helium atom. Put the glued sesame seed clump inside the fiberfill. Put 2 poppy-seed electrons inside the fiberfill close to the nucleus and place the other 8 poppy-seed electrons on the outside of the fiberfill in a random arrangement.

Questions

1. In the models, what particles do the colored and plain sesame seeds represent? What particles do the poppy seeds represent?

   _____

   _____

2. What does the fiberfill represent in the models?

   _____

3. In an atomic model, what particles are found inside the nucleus of an atom?

   _____

4. In an atomic model, what particles are found in the area surrounding the nucleus?

   _____

Name _____   Date _____

Atoms Assessment

Write your answer to the following question, and then give this paper to your teacher to grade.

1. Explain how models of the atom have changed over time. Tell how each of these scientists described the structure of an atom. Then, explain why these views have changed.
    Dalton – Thomson – Rutherford – Bohr

    _____

    _____

    _____

    _____

    _____

    _____

    _____

    _____

    _____

    _____

    _____

    _____

Student Guide
Lesson 2: Atomic and Mass Numbers

Lesson Objectives

- Define atomic number.
- Compare atomic number with the atomic mass of an element.
- Explain how an isotope of an element has the same number of protons but a different number of neutrons in the nucleus.
- Recognize that isotopes of an element typically have many similar characteristics.

PREPARE

Approximate lesson time is 60 minutes.

Materials

For the Student

   🖥 Labeling an Atom Using Atomic and Mass Numbers

   🖥 Periodic Table of Elements

Keywords and Pronunciation

atomic mass : the measure of the mass of an atom, generally the sum of the protons and neutrons; this term is used when referring to a single atom or atoms of a single isotope

atomic number : the number of protons in every atom of an element

isotope (IY-suh-tohp) : one of two or more atoms of the same element that have the same number of protons but different numbers of neutrons

LEARN
Activity 1: Atomic and Mass Numbers *(Online)*

Activity 2: Labeling an Atom Using Atomic and Mass Numbers *(Online)*

ASSESS

Lesson Assessment: Atomic and Mass Numbers, Part 1 (*Online*)

You will complete an online assessment covering the main objectives of this lesson. Your assessment will be scored by the computer.

Lesson Assessment: Atomic and Mass Numbers, Part 2 (*Offline*)

You will complete an offline assessment covering the main objectives of this lesson. Your learning coach will score this assessment.

Lesson Assessment: Atomic and Mass Numbers, Part 2

Name _____   Date _____

Labeling an Atom Using Atomic and Mass Numbers

Procedure

Label each of the lettered spaces on the diagram of the nickel atom. Next, label the 4 pieces of information found on the box from the periodic table. Use the words in the Word Bank.

Word Bank

electron   neutron   proton   orbital

atomic number   atomic mass   symbol   element name

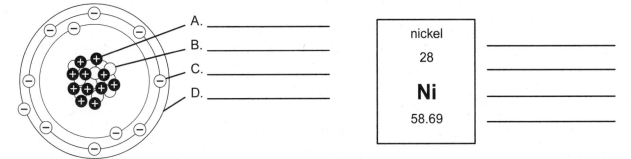

A. _____

B. _____

C. _____

D. _____

nickel

28

Ni

58.69

_____

_____

_____

_____

Questions

Use your printed copy of the Periodic Table of Elements to answer the following questions.

1. If one electron was removed from the helium atom, what would be its electrical charge?

    _____

2. If one proton was removed from the helium atom, what would be its electrical charge?

    _____

3. If one neutron was removed from the helium atom, what would be its electrical charge?

    _____

4. What information is given by the atomic number of an element?

    _____

5. What does the atomic mass tell you about an element?

    _____

Name

Date

Periodic Table of Elements

hydrogen 1 **H** 1.01																	helium 2 **He** 4.00
lithium 3 **Li** 6.94	beryllium 4 **Be** 9.01											boron 5 **B** 10.81	carbon 6 **C** 12.01	nitrogen 7 **N** 14.01	oxygen 8 **O** 15.99	fluorine 9 **F** 18.99	neon 10 **Ne** 20.18
sodium 11 **Na** 22.99	magnesium 12 **Mg** 24.31											aluminum 13 **Al** 26.98	silicon 14 **Si** 28.09	phosphorus 15 **P** 30.97	sulfur 16 **S** 32.07	chlorine 17 **Cl** 35.45	argon 18 **Ar** 39.95
potassium 19 **K** 39.10	calcium 20 **Ca** 40.08	scandium 21 **Sc** 44.96	titanium 22 **Ti** 47.87	vanadium 23 **V** 50.94	chromium 24 **Cr** 51.99	manganese 25 **Mn** 54.94	iron 26 **Fe** 55.85	cobalt 27 **Co** 58.93	nickel 28 **Ni** 58.69	copper 29 **Cu** 63.55	zinc 30 **Zn** 65.41	gallium 31 **Ga** 69.72	germanium 32 **Ge** 72.64	arsenic 33 **As** 74.92	selenium 34 **Se** 78.96	bromine 35 **Br** 79.91	krypton 36 **Kr** 83.80
rubidium 37 **Rb** 82.47	strontium 38 **Sr** 87.62	yttrium 39 **Y** 88.91	zirconium 40 **Zr** 91.22	niobium 41 **Nb** 92.91	molybdenum 42 **Mo** 95.94	technetium 43 **Tc** 98	ruthenium 44 **Ru** 101.07	rhodium 45 **Rh** 102.91	palladium 46 **Pd** 106.42	silver 47 **Ag** 107.87	cadmium 48 **Cd** 112.41	indium 49 **In** 114.82	tin 50 **Sn** 118.71	antimony 51 **Sb** 121.76	tellurium 52 **Te** 127.6	iodine 53 **I** 126.90	xenon 54 **Xe** 131.29
cesium 55 **Cs** 132.91	barium 56 **Ba** 137.34	lutetium 71 **Lu** 174.97	hafnium 72 **Hf** 178.49	tantalum 73 **Ta** 180.94	tungsten 74 **W** 183.84	rhenium 75 **Re** 186.21	osmium 76 **Os** 190.23	iridium 77 **Ir** 192.22	platinum 78 **Pt** 195.08	gold 79 **Au** 196.97	mercury 80 **Hg** 200.59	thallium 81 **Tl** 204.38	lead 82 **Pb** 207.19	bismuth 83 **Bi** 208.98	polonium 84 **Po** 209	astatine 85 **At** 210	radon 86 **Rn** 222
francium 87 **Fr** 223	radium 88 **Ra** 226.03	lawrencium 103 **Lr** 262	rutherfordium 104 **Rf** 261	dubnium 105 **Db** 262	seaborgium 106 **Sg** 266	bohrium 107 **Bh** 264	hassium 108 **Hs** 269	meitnerium 109 **Mt** 268	ununnilium 110 **Uun** 271	unununium 111 **Uuu** 272	ununbium 112 **Uub** 285		ununquadium 114 **Uuq** 289		ununhexium 116 **Uuh** ?		ununoctium 118 **Uuo** ?

lanthanum 57 **La** 138.91	cerium 58 **Ce** 140.11	praseodymium 59 **Pr** 140.91	neodymium 60 **Nd** 144.24	promethium 61 **Pm** 146.92	samarium 62 **Sm** 150.36	europium 63 **Eu** 151.96	gadolinium 64 **Gd** 157.25	terbium 65 **Tb** 158.92	dysprosium 66 **Dy** 162.50	holmium 67 **Ho** 164.93	erbium 68 **Er** 167.26	thulium 69 **Tm** 168.93	ytterbium 70 **Yb** 173.04
actinium 89 **Ac** 227	thorium 90 **Th** 232.04	protactinium 91 **Pa** 231.04	uranium 92 **U** 238.03	neptunium 93 **Np** 237	plutonium 94 **Pu** 244	americium 95 **Am** 243	curium 96 **Cm** 247	berkelium 97 **Bk** 247	californium 98 **Cf** 251	einsteinium 99 **Es** 252	fermium 100 **Fm** 257	mendelevium 101 **Md** 258	nobelium 102 **No** 259

40

Name _____   Date _____

Atomic and Mass Numbers Assessment

1. Explain how atoms of the same element can be different. Would these atoms have different chemical properties? Explain why or why not.

    _____

    _____

    _____

    _____

2. What is radioactive decay?

    _____

    _____

    _____

    _____

Student Guide
Lesson 4: Elements and the Periodic Table

Lesson Objectives

- Identify elements as the basic building blocks of matter.
- Describe the historical development of the periodic table, including Mendeleev's contributions, based on physical characteristics.
- Explain how the arrangement of elements in the periodic table now reflects the number of protons and electrons in atoms.

PREPARE

Approximate lesson time is 60 minutes.

Materials

For the Student

- Elements and the Periodic Table Review
- Periodic Table of Elements
- It's a Periodic Mystery!

Keywords and Pronunciation

family : a grouping of elements that share certain general characteristics

group : each of the 18 vertical columns of the periodic table

period : a horizontal row of the periodic table

periodic law : states that the properties of elements are periodic, or recurring, and are correlated to atomic numbers

---

LEARN
Activity 1: Elements and the Periodic Table (Online)

Activity 2: Elements and the Periodic Table (Online)

Review what you have learned about elements and the periodic table. Start by printing the review document. You may use your copy of the Periodic Table of Elements from Lesson 2 or print a new copy if needed. When you are finished, place your completed lesson review sheet in your Science Notebook.

Activity 3: It's a Periodic Mystery! *(Online)*

It's time to practice using the periodic table. Print the worksheet, It's a Periodic Mystery!, then use it and the Periodic Table of Elements to find the mystery elements in this activity.

ASSESS

Lesson Assessment: Elements and the Periodic Table, Part 1 *(Offline)*

You will complete an offline assessment covering the main objectives of this lesson. Your learning coach will score this assessment.

Lesson Assessment: Elements and the Periodic Table, Part 2 *(Offline)*

You will complete an offline assessment covering the main objectives of this lesson. Your learning coach will score this assessment.

Name _____   Date _____

Periodic Table of Elements

Period	1	2	3	4	5	6	7	8	9	10	11	12	13	14	15	16	17	18
1	hydrogen 1 H 1.01																	helium 2 He 4.00
2	lithium 3 Li 6.94	beryllium 4 Be 9.01											boron 5 B 10.81	carbon 6 C 12.01	nitrogen 7 N 14.01	oxygen 8 O 15.99	fluorine 9 F 18.99	neon 10 Ne 20.18
3	sodium 11 Na 22.99	magnesium 12 Mg 24.31											aluminum 13 Al 26.98	silicon 14 Si 28.09	phosphorus 15 P 30.97	sulfur 16 S 32.07	chlorine 17 Cl 35.45	argon 18 Ar 39.95
4	potassium 19 K 39.10	calcium 20 Ca 40.08	scandium 21 Sc 44.96	titanium 22 Ti 47.87	vanadium 23 V 50.94	chromium 24 Cr 51.99	manganese 25 Mn 54.94	iron 26 Fe 55.85	cobalt 27 Co 58.93	nickel 28 Ni 58.69	copper 29 Cu 63.55	zinc 30 Zn 65.41	gallium 31 Ga 69.72	germanium 32 Ge 72.64	arsenic 33 As 74.92	selenium 34 Se 78.96	bromine 35 Br 79.91	krypton 36 Kr 83.80
5	rubidium 37 Rb 82.47	strontium 38 Sr 87.62	yttrium 39 Y 88.91	zirconium 40 Zr 91.22	niobium 41 Nb 92.91	molybdenum 42 Mo 95.94	technetium 43 Tc 98	ruthenium 44 Ru 101.07	rhodium 45 Rh 102.91	palladium 46 Pd 106.42	silver 47 Ag 107.87	cadmium 48 Cd 112.41	indium 49 In 114.82	tin 50 Sn 118.71	antimony 51 Sb 121.76	tellurium 52 Te 127.6	iodine 53 I 126.90	xenon 54 Xe 131.29
6	cesium 55 Cs 132.91	barium 56 Ba 137.34	lutetium 71 Lu 174.97	hafnium 72 Hf 178.49	tantalum 73 Ta 180.94	tungsten 74 W 183.84	rhenium 75 Re 186.21	osmium 76 Os 190.23	iridium 77 Ir 192.22	platinum 78 Pt 195.08	gold 79 Au 196.97	mercury 80 Hg 200.59	thallium 81 Tl 204.38	lead 82 Pb 207.19	bismuth 83 Bi 208.98	polonium 84 Po 209	astatine 85 At 210	radon 86 Rn 222
7	francium 87 Fr 223	radium 88 Ra 226.03	lawrencium 103 Lr 262	rutherfordium 104 Rf 261	dubnium 105 Db 262	seaborgium 106 Sg 266	bohrium 107 Bh 264	hassium 108 Hs 269	meitnerium 109 Mt 268	ununnilium 110 Uun 271	unununium 111 Uuu 272	ununbium 112 Uub 285		ununquadium 114 Uuq 289		ununhexium 116 Uuh ?		ununoctium 118 Uuo ?

lanthanum 57 La 138.91	cerium 58 Ce 140.11	praseodymium 59 Pr 140.91	neodymium 60 Nd 144.24	promethium 61 Pm 146.92	samarium 62 Sm 150.36	europium 63 Eu 151.96	gadolinium 64 Gd 157.25	terbium 65 Tb 158.92	dysprosium 66 Dy 162.50	holmium 67 Ho 164.93	erbium 68 Er 167.26	thulium 69 Tm 168.93	ytterbium 70 Yb 173.04
actinium 89 Ac 227	thorium 90 Th 232.04	protactinium 91 Pa 231.04	uranium 92 U 238.03	neptunium 93 Np 237	plutonium 94 Pu 244	americium 95 Am 243	curium 96 Cm 247	berkelium 97 Bk 247	californium 98 Cf 251	einsteinium 99 Es 252	fermium 100 Fm 257	mendelevium 101 Md 258	nobelium 102 No 259

Name _____   Date _____

Elements and the Periodic Table Review

Nine chemical elements are listed below in alphabetical order.

argon (Ar)

beryllium (Be)

calcium (Ca)

krypton (Kr)

magnesium (Mg)

neon (Ne)

oxygen (O)

selenium (Se)

sulfur (S)

1. These elements belong to three different periods in the periodic table. Arrange the elements by those found in the same period. You may write just the symbol of the element.

    a.

    b.

    c.

2. Now arrange the elements according to the three periodic table groups to which they belong.

    a.

    b.

    c.

3. Now arrange the elements into the following groups: metals, nonmetals, and noble gases.

    a. metals:

    b. nonmetals:

    c. noble gases:

4. This is the square from the periodic table for the element helium (He). Identify three pieces of information you can learn about helium from the two numbers in the square.

    a.

    b.

    c.

    | helium |
    | 2 |
    | **He** |
    | 4.003 |

Name _____   Date _____

It's a Periodic Mystery!

Procedure

1. Use your copy of the Periodic Table of Elements to obtain information about each element in the Mystery Clues list. Record your information on the Mystery Clues Data Table.

Mystery Clues

A. This element has 20 electrons when the atom is electrically neutral.

B. This element is an alkaline-earth metals group. It has 12 protons.

C. This element is the only member in its group as a gas at room temperature and norma pressure. It has 8 electrons when the atom is electrically neutral.

D. An isotope of this element has 20 neutrons and a mass number of 39.

E. This isotope is a transition metal in Group 8 and has 26 electrons when the atom is electrically neutral.

F. This element belongs to the same group as aluminum (Al) and is a metalloid. It is ingroup 13.

Mystery Clues Data Table

Letter of Mystery Element	Atomic Number	Average Atomic Mass	Category (metal, non-metal, etc.)	Number of Protons	Number of Electrons in an Electrically Neutral Atom	Element Name and Symbol
A						
B						
C						
D						
E						
F						

Name _____ Date _____

Elements and the Periodic Table Assessment

6.   Look at the two squares from the Periodic Table and answer the questions.

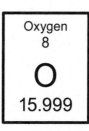

| Nitrogen 7 N 14.007 | Oxygen 8 O 15.999 |

a.   Are these two boxes located next to each other in the Periodic Table? How do you know?

_____

_____

b.   Where do you find the symbol for the element?

_____

c.   What information is provided by the decimal numbers?

_____

d.   If nitrogen and oxygen are in the same row, what do you know about their properties?

_____

_____

Student Guide
Lesson 5: Design of the Periodic Table

Lesson Objectives

- Describe the design of the periodic table and explain how elements are grouped (e.g., families and periods).
- Interpret a diagram that displays information about a specific element (e.g., symbol, atomic number, name of element, and atomic mass.
- Identify areas of the periodic table that group metals, nonmetals, and inert gases.

PREPARE

Approximate lesson time is 60 minutes.

Materials

For the Student

- 🖳 Boiling Points and Melting Points
- 🖳 Data Table
- 🖳 Graph Paper
- 🖳 Periodic Table of Elements
  - colored pencils - red, blue, green, orange, black
  - ruler, metric

LEARN
Activity 1: Design of the Periodic Table *(Online)*

Activity 2: Boiling Points and Melting Points *(Online)*

ASSESS

Lesson Assessment: Design of The Periodic Table, Part 1 (*Online*)

You will complete an offline assessment covering the main objectives of this lesson. Your learning coach will score this assessment.

Lesson Assessment: Design of the Periodic Table, Part 2 (*Offline*)

You will complete an offline assessment covering the main objectives of this lesson. Your learning coach will score this assessment.

Name _____   Date _____

Graph Paper

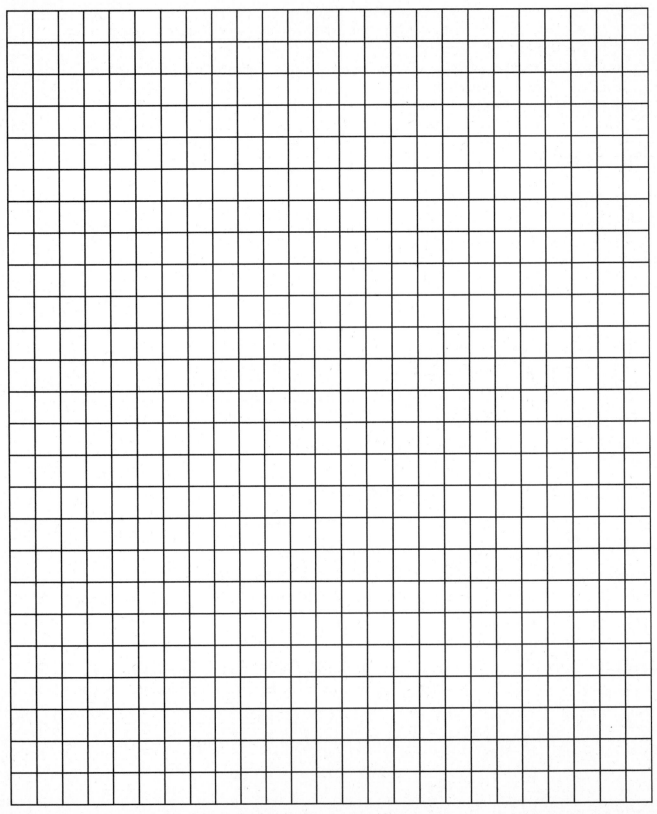

Name _____   Date _____

Data Table

Atomic number	Name	Melting Point (K)	Boiling Point (K)
1	Hydrogen	14.01	20.28
2	Helium	0.95	4.216
3	Lithium	453.69	1590
4	Beryllium	1551	3243
5	Boron	2573	2823
6	Carbon	3823	5100
7	Nitrogen	63.29	77.4
8	Oxygen	54.75	90.188
9	Fluorine	53.53	85.01
10	Neon	24.48	27.1
11	Sodium	370.95	1165
12	Magnesium	921.95	1380
13	Aluminum	933.52	2740
14	Silicon	1683	2628
15	Phosphorus	317.3	553
16	Sulfur	386	717.824
17	Chlorine	172.17	238.55
18	Argon	83.78	87.29
19	Potassium	336.8	1047
20	Calcium	1112	1760

All of the above data is at a pressure of one atmosphere.

Name _____ Date _____

Periodic Table

Element	Symbol	Atomic #	Atomic Mass
hydrogen	H	1	1.01
helium	He	2	4.00
lithium	Li	3	6.94
beryllium	Be	4	9.01
boron	B	5	10.81
carbon	C	6	12.01
nitrogen	N	7	14.01
oxygen	O	8	15.99
fluorine	F	9	18.99
neon	Ne	10	20.18
sodium	Na	11	22.99
magnesium	Mg	12	24.31
aluminum	Al	13	26.98
silicon	Si	14	28.09
phosphorus	P	15	30.97
sulfur	S	16	32.07
chlorine	Cl	17	35.45
argon	Ar	18	39.95
potassium	K	19	39.10
calcium	Ca	20	40.08
scandium	Sc	21	44.96
titanium	Ti	22	47.87
vanadium	V	23	50.94
chromium	Cr	24	51.99
manganese	Mn	25	54.94
iron	Fe	26	55.85
cobalt	Co	27	58.93
nickel	Ni	28	58.69
copper	Cu	29	63.55
zinc	Zn	30	65.41
gallium	Ga	31	69.72
germanium	Ge	32	72.64
arsenic	As	33	74.92
selenium	Se	34	78.96
bromine	Br	35	79.91
krypton	Kr	36	83.80
rubidium	Rb	37	82.47
strontium	Sr	38	87.62
yttrium	Y	39	88.91
zirconium	Zr	40	91.22
niobium	Nb	41	92.91
molybdenum	Mo	42	95.94
technetium	Tc	43	98
ruthenium	Ru	44	101.07
rhodium	Rh	45	102.91
palladium	Pd	46	106.42
silver	Ag	47	107.87
cadmium	Cd	48	112.41
indium	In	49	114.82
tin	Sn	50	118.71
antimony	Sb	51	121.76
tellurium	Te	52	127.6
iodine	I	53	126.90
xenon	Xe	54	131.29
cesium	Cs	55	132.91
barium	Ba	56	137.34
lutetium	Lu	71	174.97
hafnium	Hf	72	178.49
tantalum	Ta	73	180.94
tungsten	W	74	183.84
rhenium	Re	75	186.21
osmium	Os	76	190.23
iridium	Ir	77	192.22
platinum	Pt	78	195.08
gold	Au	79	196.97
mercury	Hg	80	200.59
thallium	Tl	81	204.38
lead	Pb	82	207.19
bismuth	Bi	83	208.98
polonium	Po	84	209
astatine	At	85	210
radon	Rn	86	222
cesium	Cs	55	132.91
francium	Fr	87	223
radium	Ra	88	226.03
lawrencium	Lr	103	262
rutherfordium	Rf	104	261
dubnium	Db	105	262
seaborgium	Sg	106	266
bohrium	Bh	107	264
hassium	Hs	108	269
meitnerium	Mt	109	268
ununnillium	Uun	110	271
unununium	Uuu	111	272
ununbium	Uub	112	285
ununquadium	Uuq	114	289
ununhexium	Uuh	116	?
ununoctium	Uuo	118	?

Lanthanides:

Element	Symbol	Atomic #	Atomic Mass
lanthanum	La	57	138.91
cerium	Ce	58	140.11
praseodymium	Pr	59	140.91
neodymium	Nd	60	144.24
promethium	Pm	61	146.92
samarium	Sm	62	150.36
europium	Eu	63	151.96
gadolinium	Gd	64	157.25
terbium	Tb	65	158.92
dysprosium	Dy	66	162.50
holmium	Ho	67	164.93
erbium	Er	68	167.26
thulium	Tm	69	168.93
ytterbium	Yb	70	173.04

Actinides:

Element	Symbol	Atomic #	Atomic Mass
actinium	Ac	89	227
thorium	Th	90	232.04
protactinium	Pa	91	231.04
uranium	U	92	238.03
neptunium	Np	93	237
plutonium	Pu	94	244
americium	Am	95	243
curium	Cm	96	247
berkelium	Bk	97	247
californium	Cf	98	251
einsteinium	Es	99	252
fermium	Fm	100	257
mendelevium	Md	101	258
nobelium	No	102	259

Name   Date

Boiling Points and Melting Points

Introduction

The melting point of a substance is the temperature at which a heated substance changes from solid to liquid. The boiling point is the temperature at which a substance changes from liquid to gas. The melting and boiling points of a given substance will vary if the pressure of the environment around the substance changes. Melting and boiling points of substances are given at a standard pressure of 1 atmosphere (atm).

In expressing temperature as a numeric value, remember that scientists use the Kelvin scale. The Kelvin scale begins at absolute 0 (0 K), which is a theoretical temperature at which atoms cease to move. As an example, the melting point of water is 273 K.

Purpose

In this activity you will compare boiling points and melting points of different elements and will identify trends in the periodic table.

Materials

graph paper
colored pencils (red, blue, green, orange, and black)
straightedge

Tips for Completing This Activity

- Take your time as you graph the data points, being sure to keep the boiling point data and melting point data on the separate lines.

- It may be helpful if you write the corresponding element symbol below each atomic number so you don't have to constantly refer back to the Periodic Table.

Procedures

1. Print out the Data Table and look over the data provided. This data is for both melting points and boiling points of various elements.

2. On the graph paper, draw a set of axes to begin a graph. Your graph will have positive values only, so you only need to show one quadrant. Label the vertical or *y* axis Temperature (K). Label the horizontal or *x* axis Atomic Number.

3. Make tick marks along each axis and label the tick marks with appropriate numerical values.

- To decide what these values should be, look at the largest and smallest values that appear in the Data Table.

- Each axis should begin at 0 and should accommodate values a little larger than the largest value in the Data Table.

- Marks on the axis should be as frequent as possible without overcrowding the line and making it difficult to read the graph.

Name _____   Date _____

4. You will create two line plots on the same graph. To do this, use a red colored pencil to begin plotting the boiling point data on the graph paper. Make small solid circles (•) for each data point. When you have plotted all the data points, go back and connect the circles to make it into a line plot.

5. Repeat Step 4 using a blue colored pencil for the melting point data and open circles (O) to plot points. When you are finished, you should have two line plots on the same set of axes.

6. Using a black colored pencil, draw a square around the data points representing both the boiling points and melting points for helium and neon. The atomic numbers for these elements are 2 and 10.

7. Using a green colored pencil, circle the data points representing both the boiling point and melting point for lithium, sodium, and potassium (atomic numbers 3, and 11, and 19).

8. Connect the three green-circled data points for boiling points with a green line, then connect the three green-circled data points for the melting points.

9. Use an orange colored pencil to draw a straight line across the graph at 298K which is the temperature value for room temperature.

Analysis and Conclusions

1. Looking at the line plots on your graph, describe how boiling point and melting point vary with respect to atomic number.

    _____

    _____

2. Now look at the segment of the graph between the two data points marked with black squares. Describe how the boiling point and melting point plots behave between these points. Be as specific as possible.

    _____

    _____

    _____

3. On your graph, the data points between the black squares are data for elements with atomic numbers 3 through 9. Locate these elements on your periodic table. What term or description would you use to identify these elements with respect to the periodic table?

    _____

    _____

4. Now look at the green lines you created by connecting the three boiling point data points and the three melting point data points. For each of these lines, describe any trends you see.

    _____

    _____

Name _____   Date _____

5. Locate the elements on your periodic table that you circled in green on your graph. What term or description would you use to identify these elements with respect to the periodic table?

    _____

    _____

6. After reviewing your answers to Questions 2 and 4, would you define boiling point and melting point as a periodic table family trend (vertical groups), period trend (horizontal rows), or neither? Explain your answer.

    _____

    _____

    _____

7. Using the room temperature line (orange line) and your periodic table, make lists that identify the state of matter (gas, liquid, or solid) in which each element you plotted exists at room temperature. Explain your answers.

    _____

    _____

    _____

    _____

    _____

Name _____   Date _____

Design of The Periodic Table Assessment

1. What pattern appears in the horizontal arrangement (rows) of the elements in the Periodic Table, moving from left to right?

   _____

   _____

2. What pattern appears in the vertical arrangement (columns) of the elements in the Periodic Table, moving from top to bottom?

   _____

   _____

3. What data is given inside each box on the Periodic Table? Fill in the blanks to tell what each piece of data represents.

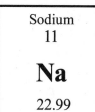

   a. _____ = atomic number

   b. _____ = symbol for the element

   c. _____ = name of element

   d. _____ = atomic mass

Student Guide
Lesson 6: Molecules

Lesson Objectives

- Define a molecule as two or more atoms that share electrons in a chemical bond.
- Explain that a molecule is the smallest particle of a compound with all the properties of that substance.
- Describe chemical bonding as the formation of new substances through the combination of the atoms of specific elements.

PREPARE

Approximate lesson time is 60 minutes.

Materials

For the Student

- Molecules Review
- Molecules for Good Health

Keywords and Pronunciation

chemical changes : changes in matter that involve changes in the types of molecules present, in which bonds between atoms are broken and/or formed

compounds : substances containing atoms of two or more elements

molecule (MAH-lih-kyool) : The smallest bit into which a chemical substance can be divided and still have the properties of that substance. Molecules of water contain hydrogen and oxygen atoms.

physical changes : changes in matter that involve changes in the relationships among the molecules and/or in their motions, but not in the compounds or elements present

---

LEARN
Activity 1: Molecules *(Online)*

Activity 2: Molecules *(Online)*

Activity 3: Molecules for Good Health *(Online)*

ASSESS

Lesson Assessment: Molecules, Part 1 (*Online*)

You will complete an online assessment covering the main objectives of this lesson. Your assessment will be scored by the computer.

Lesson Assessment: Molecules, Part 2 (*Offline*)

You will complete an offline assessment covering the main objectives of this lesson. Your learning coach will score this assessment.

Lesson Assessment: Molecules, Part 2 (*Offline*)

Name _____   Date _____

Molecules Review

Use the words from this list to fill in the blanks to answer 1–4.

atom

compound

element

molecule

1. What is the term for matter that consists of two or more atoms? _____

2. Matter that is made of only one kind of atom is called what? _____

3. What do scientists call a substance that contains atoms from two or more elements that are chemically bonded? _____

4. What term is used for the particle that can be combined to form molecules?

   _____

Look at the models below. Select TWO words from the following list that can describe each model: atom, compound, element, and molecule. Write the two words that apply to each model on the lines provided.

5. ○

   _____
   _____

6. ⬭

   _____
   _____

7. ⬭

   _____
   _____

Name _____   Date _____

Molecules for Good Health

Materials

Periodic Table of Elements

Procedure

1. Read each vitamin name and the molecule that is used in each vitamin.

2. Using the periodic table, find the elements that make up the molecules. List the elements on the chart.

3. Next to the name of the element, list the number of atoms used in the molecule.

Vitamin	Molecule	Element and Number of Atoms
Vitamin B1	$C_{12}H_{19}OS$	
Vitamin B12	$C_{63}H_{88}CoN_{14}O_{14}P$	
Vitamin C	$C_6H_8O_6$	
Vitamin D3	$C_{27}H_{44}O$	
Vitamin E	$C_{29}H_{50}O_2$	
Vitamin H	$C_{10}H_{16}N_2O_3S$	

Name _____ Date _____

Vitamin K1	$C_{31}H_{46}O_2$	
Vitamin U	$C_6H_{15}NO_2S$	

Name _____   Date _____

Molecules Assessment

Write your answers to the following questions, then give the paper to your teacher to grade.

1. How does an iron nail become a rusty nail?

    _____

    _____

    _____

    _____

2. Identify H_2 and describe its properties.

    _____

    _____

    _____

    _____

Student Guide
Lesson 7: Properties of Matter

Lesson Objectives
- Differentiate physical and chemical properties of matter.
- Give examples of physical properties of substances.
- Give examples of chemical properties of substances.

PREPARE

Approximate lesson time is 60 minutes.

Advance Preparation
- If you don't already have it, you will need an empty 0.5 liter bottle (or any other drink bottle), cotton balls, and two blocks of wood; one medium-sized (about 20 cm of a 2 x 4) and one small (about 10 cm of a 2 x 4) for this activity.

Materials
   For the Student
   > How Dense?
   bottle, plastic - 0.5 liter (water or any other drink bottle)
   cotton balls
   block, medium wooden - about 20 cm of a 2 x 4
   block, small wooden - about 10 cm of a 2 x 4
   digital balance
   ruler, metric
   > Lesson Review

Keywords and Pronunciation
atom : A tiny particle that is the fundamental building block of substances. The properties of the atom determine the properties of the element made up only of those atoms.

boiling point : the temperature at which a liquid becomes a gas

chemical properties : properties of a substance relating to the chemical nature and reactivity of the substance

density : the mass per unit volume of a substance

element : a type of atom, with a particular number of protons in the nucleus; a pure substance with only one type of atom throughout

malleable (MA-lee-uh-buhl) : Able to be hammered out. Aluminum is so malleable that it can be hammered out into a thin foil.

matter : anything that takes up space and has mass; the three usual forms of matter are solid, liquid, and gas

melting point : the temperature at which a solid becomes a liquid

physical properties : the properties of a substance that can be observed without changing the chemical makeup of the substance

solubility (sahl-yuh-BIH-luh-tee) : How much solute can be dissolved in a solvent at a given temperature. The solubility of the sugar increased when we raised the temperature.

---

thermal conduction : The passing of heat energy through a solid, liquid, or gas by collisions of molecules. When I touched the hot water pipe, thermal conduction allowed me to feel heat energy from the hot water inside.

LEARN
Activity 1: Matter Has Properties *(Online)*

Activity 2: How Dense? *(Online)*

Activity 3: Properties of Matter *(Online)*
Review what you have learned about properties of matter. When finished, place your completed lesson review sheet in your Science Notebook.

ASSESS
Lesson Assessment: Properties of Matter (*Online*)
You will complete an online assessment covering the main objectives of this lesson. Your assessment will be scored by the computer.

Name _____ Date _____

How Dense?

Materials

empty film canister with lid

cotton balls

medium-size block of wood (about 20 cm of a 2x4)

small block of wood (about 10 cm of a 2x4)

metric ruler

digital balance

Procedure

Part A

1. Fill the empty film canister loosely with cotton balls.

2. Put the lid on and determine the mass of the closed canister with the cotton balls inside by using a balance.

3. Record this mass in the appropriate spot in Data Table 1.

4. The volume of a standard film canister is approximately 35 cm³. Assume this is the volume of your canister. Record this as the volume of the film canister with cotton balls in the appropriate location in Data Table 1.

5. Remove the lid of the film canister.

6. Even though the canister is "full" of cotton balls, you should find that you can stuff more into the canister (much like you can always pack more clothes into a suitcase!). Pack as many cotton balls into the canister as possible, while still being able to place the lid back on.

7. With the lid securely on, use the balance to determine the mass of the canister stuffed full of cotton balls. Record the value in Data Table 1.

8. Record the assumed volume of this canister as well. (Think, did the volume change?)

9. Calculate the density of the film canister filled with just a few cotton balls by dividing the mass by the volume. Record the density in the space provided in Data Table 1.

10. Repeat the density calculation for the film canister stuffed full of many cotton balls. Again, record this value in Data Table 1.

Part B

11. Using a ruler, measure the width, height, and length of the medium-size block of wood. Be sure to record these values in centimeters in Data Table 2.

12. Calculate the volume of this wood block by multiplying width times length times height. Record this value, in centimeters cubed (cm³), in Data Table 2.

13. Determine the mass of the wooden block on the balance and record this value.

14. Calculate the density of the block and record the value in Data Table 2.

15. Using a ruler, measure the width, height, and length of the small block of wood. Be sure to record these values in centimeters in Data Table 2.

16. Repeat steps 12-14 with the small block, recording the values in the appropriate locations in Data Table 2.

Data Table 1

Trial	Mass (g)	Volume (cm³)	Density (g/cm³)
1. Film canister with a few cotton balls			
2. Film canister packed with cotton balls			

Data Table 2

Block of wood	Height of block (cm)	Length of block (cm)	Width of block (cm)	Volume of block (cm³)	Mass of block (g)	Density of block (g/cm³)
Large block						
Small block						

Questions

1. In calculating density of the tightly packed film canister, you assumed it was the volume of a "standard" canister. How would your density calculations for the film canister change if the assumption were not accurate? For example, what if the volume of the canister was smaller than you assumed?

   _____

   _____

   _____

2. Considering mass, volume, and density, which of these variables changed between the two different trials of the film canister in Part A? Which remained constant?

   _____

_____

_____

3. Considering mass, volume, and density, which of these variables changed between the two wooden blocks of different sizes in Part B? Which remained constant?

_____

_____

4. Imagine you have a piece of Styrofoam. Suppose you squeezed this Styrofoam hard enough to change its shape. Briefly describe how this compression would affect its mass, volume, and density.

_____

_____

_____

_____

5. A golf ball and a ping pong ball are approximately the same volume. However, a golf ball has much more mass. Which ball is denser? Explain your answer.

_____

_____

6. Suppose that instead of using a block that was half the size of the medium-size block, you had squashed it down in a very strong vice so the block takes up half the volume it did before. How do you think its density would have been affected?

_____

_____

_____

7. Write a few sentences to summarize how density is changed by changing the mass without changing the volume, and by changing the volume of a substance without changing the mass (both by increasing and decreasing). If you prefer, you can use specific numbers and calculations to show the relationship instead.

_____

_____

_____

_____

_____

Name _____   Date _____

Properties of Matter Lesson Review

The story below describes a number of properties of materials. Write P after the changes related to physical properties and C after changes related to chemical properties.

A slice of bread and a slice of cheese were left on a kitchen counter overnight. The bread became too **dried out** ☐ to eat, and the cheese became too **moldy** ☐ to eat. The cheese and bread were both thrown on a compost heap. One night a rat ate and **digested** ☐ the cheese, but the bread slowly **decomposed** ☐ . The next spring the compost was **spread** ☐ on a garden, and the remains of the bread **became part** ☐ of a tomato plant. As the tomato plant **grew taller** ☐ , its tomatoes **became larger** ☐ and **heavier** ☐ . The tomatoes **tasted** ☐ quite good, but the rat ate most of them, too.

Student Guide
Lesson 8: States of Matter

Lesson Objectives

- Identify different states of matter.
- Describe how atoms and the arrangement of atoms contribute to the properties and states of matter.
- Explain how molecular motion differs in solids, liquids, and gases.

PREPARE

Approximate lesson time is 60 minutes.

Advance Preparation

- If you don't already have it, you will need a plastic syringe with plunger and cap (10mL capacity) for the Getting in Hot Water activity in this lesson.

Materials

For the Student

  🖳 Getting in Hot Water

    pan

    pot holder

    plastic syringe with plunger - and cap (10 mL capacity)

    thermometer

    water

Keywords and Pronunciation

gas : matter with no definite shape, but that takes the shape of its container and fills it completely; usually invisible

liquid : Something that flows freely and takes the shape of its container. We know water is a liquid because we can pour it, and it takes the shape of whatever container we put it in.

solid : something with a definite shape that is not easily changed

LEARN
Activity 1: States of Matter *(Online)*

Activity 2: Getting in Hot Water *(Online)*

Safety

When completing the activity, Getting in Hot Water, make sure you use the potholders to protect your hands when using the syringe. Exercise care while you are drawing the warm water into the syringe and then expelling it out of the syringe.

ASSESS

Lesson Assessment: States of Matter (*Online*)

You will complete an online assessment covering the main objectives of this lesson. Your assessment will be scored by the computer.

Name _____   Date _____

Getting in Hot Water

Materials

thermometer (not digital)

pan

potholders

water

plastic syringe with plunger and cap, 10 mL capacity (found in drugstores)

Procedure

1. First, determine the atmospheric pressure in your area. You can find this information in a local newspaper or a web site for a local television news station. Once you have the right information, record the atmospheric pressure (in inches of mercury) in your Science Notebook.

2. Convert the atmospheric pressure from inches (of mercury) to atmospheres (abbreviation: atm), which is a more common unit in science. To do this, divide the pressure in inches by 29.92. This will give you the pressure in your area in atm. Record this pressure value in your Science Notebook.

3. Look at the phase diagram below for water.

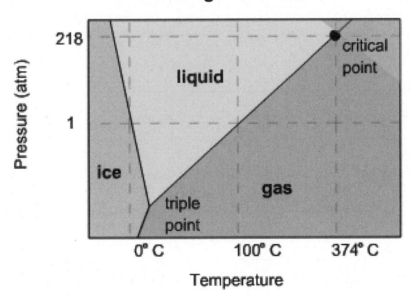

4. According to the phase diagram and your local atmospheric pressure, predict the temperature at which water will boil where you live. Record this value in your Science Notebook.

5. Fill the pan with approximately 0.25 L of water.

6. Place the pan on a stovetop and turn on the burner to high.

7. Watch the pan carefully. When you first notice small bubbles forming, place the thermometer in the pan to test the temperature of the water. Be careful not to let the glass tip of the thermometer touch the sides or bottom of the pan. Safety Tip: hold the thermometer carefully—do not put your hand or arm over the boiling water.

8. Continue to let the temperature of the water rise until the water has reached a rolling boil.

9. Record the temperature of this boiling water in your Science Notebook.

10. Let the water cool slightly in the pan, until it reaches approximately 80°C. Record the exact temperature of the water in your Science Notebook.

11. Carefully draw up 3 mL of this warm water in the plastic syringe by putting the tip of the syringe in the water and pulling back the plunger.

12. Flip the syringe upside down so that the plunger is at the bottom. Push the plunger in, expelling all the air trapped in the syringe, leaving only the 3 mL of water in the syringe.

13. Place the cap on the syringe.

14. Carefully draw back the plunger on the syringe to the maximum capacity of the syringe. Be sure not to pull it all the way out. (This may require some strength.)

15. Record your observations about the water that is trapped in the syringe.

Analysis and Conclusions

1. If your water did not boil at exactly 100°C, why not? Use the word pressure in your answer. If your water did boil at exactly 100°C, explain why.

_____

_____

_____

2. Was the measured temperature at which the water boiled in the pan the same as the predicted temperature from the phase diagram? If not, give a reason why they might have differed.

_____

_____

_____

_____

3. What happened to the water in the syringe after you pulled the plunger to full capacity?

_____

4. How was the pressure in the syringe changed when the plunger was pulled back? How would it change if the plunger were pushed in?

_____

_____

5. Use the temperature of the warm water and the phase diagram to hypothesize the atmospheric pressure of the air inside the syringe when the plunger was pulled back.

_____

_____

_____

6. You may have noticed that many food items, including frozen foods, often have alternate cooking instructions for high altitude locations. What would happen if you decided to boil some frozen peas at the top of a mountain without using the alternate cooking directions? Hint: Think about the activity with the syringe. Was the boiling water in the syringe as hot as the boiling water in the pan?

Student Guide
Lesson 9: Physical and Chemical Changes

Lesson Objectives

- Differentiate physical changes from chemical changes, in terms of the molecular structure of a substance.
- Recognize that chemical reactions release or absorb heat.
- Distinguish examples of physical and chemical changes.

PREPARE

Approximate lesson time is 60 minutes.

Advance Preparation

- If you don't already have it, you will need vinegar, clear cups (wide-mouthed), plastic wrap, and sugar cubes for this activity.

Materials

For the Student

📖 Eggcellent! Worksheet

cups - 4 wide-mouthed, clear

eggs, raw - 2

measuring cup - for liquids

plastic wrap

spoon - or tongs (long-handled)

sugar cubes - 8

vinegar, white - 2 cups

water - 2 cups

Keywords and Pronunciation

chemical changes : changes in matter that involve changes in the types of molecules present, in which bonds between atoms are broken and/or formed

conservation of energy : in closed physical systems, energy is neither created nor destroyed, but may change form or location

nuclear changes : changes in the nuclei of atoms that change elements to one or more other elements

physical changes : changes in matter that involve changes in the relationships among the molecules and/or in their motions, but not in the compounds or elements present

products : the molecules that result from a chemical reaction

reactants : the starting molecules in a chemical reaction

LEARN
Activity 1: Physical and Chemical Changes *(Online)*

Activity 2: Eggcellent! *(Online)*
You have been studying how matter can change physically and chemically. Examine the changes an egg and sugar can undergo over several days. Also examine factors that may or may not influence those changes. Gather some eggs and sugar cubes and get ready to explore!

ASSESS
Lesson Assessment: Physical and Chemical Changes (*Online*)
You will complete an online assessment covering the main objectives of this lesson. Your assessment will be scored by the computer.

Name   Date

Eggcellent!

Materials

long-handled spoon or tongs

raw eggs, 2

sugar cubes, 8

wide-mouthed clear cups, 4

white vinegar, at least 2 cups

water, at least 2 cups, at room temperature

plastic wrap

liquid measuring cup

Procedure

1. Use the spoon to place one egg in each of 2 cups, being careful not to crack the eggs.

2. Carefully measure 1 cup of white vinegar and pour it into one of the cups with an egg. Only pour the amount needed to cover the egg. Note how much liquid it takes to cover the egg and write this amount down in your Science Notebook, so you can use the same amount in the next few steps. The vinegar should cover the egg completely. If you are using larger cups, 1 cup of vinegar might not cover the egg completely. Continue to add measured amounts of vinegar until the egg is completely immersed. Be sure to measure the total volume of liquid used to cover the egg, so the same amount of liquid can be used in the other cups for comparison. This will ensure that differences in results for the different liquids are not due to differences in the amount of liquid.

3. Observe the surface of the egg closely to see if anything happens there. Write down your observations in your Science Notebook.

4. Measure 1 cup of room temperature water and pour it into the other cup with an egg, completely immersing the egg. Refer to your notes from Step 2. Pour the same amount of water over this egg as the amount of vinegar you used in Step 2. As before, observe the surface of the egg.

5. Cover the tops of both cups with plastic wrap.

6. Record your observations for both cups in your Science Notebook.

7. Place 4 sugar cubes in each of the remaining 2 cups.

8. Slowly pour the same volume of vinegar you used in Step 2 into one of the cups with sugar cubes. Watch closely what happens to the cubes.

9. Pour an identical volume of water into the other cup with sugar cubes. Again, watch what happens to the cubes.

10. Cover the tops of these cups with plastic wrap. Store at room temperature.

11. Record your observations for both cups in your Science Notebook.

12. Continue to observe each cup periodically for the next 4 days. In your Science Notebook, write down what you see, including any changes you see in the liquids around the egg or the sugar (if any remains).

Name _____ Date _____

Analysis

An eggshell is mainly composed of the compound known as calcium carbonate. When calcium carbonate comes in contact with vinegar (acetic acid), it forms calcium acetate and bubbles of carbon dioxide gas. Here is the reaction:

$2 CH_3COOH + CaCO_3 \rightarrow (CH_3COO)_2Ca + CO_2 + H_2O$
vinegar + eggshell   calcium acetate + carbon dioxide + water

Questions

1. Explain what you observed when you added the liquids to each cup.

_____

_____

_____

_____

2. Explain what you observed in each cup after 2 days had passed.

_____

_____

3. The materials in which of the cups demonstrated a chemical change? A physical change? No change?

_____

_____

_____

4. After 4 days, the eggshell should no longer be present in the vinegar. What happened to the shell? What did you observe that convinced you of this?

_____

_____

_____

Name _____   Date _____

5.   After about 1 day the sugar cubes should no longer be present in either solution. What happened to the sugar?

_____

_____

_____

_____

6.   When an eggshell comes in contact with vinegar (acetic acid) it forms calcium acetate and bubbles of carbon dioxide. Identify the main products and reactants in this reaction.

_____

_____

7.   Why was the result different between the water that contained the eggshell and the water that contained the sugar?

_____

_____

Extension

If you have time, repeat the experiment starting with cold vinegar and water and then warm vinegar and water. Do the bubbles form faster on the egg in the cold vinegar or the warm vinegar? Does the sugar dissolve faster in the cold liquid or the warm liquid?

Student Guide
Lesson 11: Unit Review

Lesson Objectives

- Distinguish between physical changes and chemical changes.
- Describe the structure of an atom, of an element, and its isotopes.
- Describe the patterns of organization represented in the periodic table.
- Describe six properties of matter.
- Explain how the motion of molecules differs in different states of matter.

PREPARE

Approximate lesson time is 60 minutes.

Materials

For the Student

- Periodic Table of Elements
- Unit Review

LEARN
Activity 1: Matter *(Online)*

You have now learned many facts about the periodic table, elements, and states of matter. This lesson will give you practice on the concepts learned in this unit. Print the Unit Review Sheet and Periodic Table. You may also access the online Periodic Table of Elements to use when completing the review sheet.

Name

Date

Periodic Table of Elements

hydrogen 1 **H** 1.01																	helium 2 **He** 4.00
lithium 3 **Li** 6.94	beryllium 4 **Be** 9.01											boron 5 **B** 10.81	carbon 6 **C** 12.01	nitrogen 7 **N** 14.01	oxygen 8 **O** 15.99	fluorine 9 **F** 18.99	neon 10 **Ne** 20.18
sodium 11 **Na** 22.99	magnesium 12 **Mg** 24.31											aluminum 13 **Al** 26.98	silicon 14 **Si** 28.09	phosphorus 15 **P** 30.97	sulfur 16 **S** 32.07	chlorine 17 **Cl** 35.45	argon 18 **Ar** 39.95
potassium 19 **K** 39.10	calcium 20 **Ca** 40.08	scandium 21 **Sc** 44.96	titanium 22 **Ti** 47.87	vanadium 23 **V** 50.94	chromium 24 **Cr** 51.99	manganese 25 **Mn** 54.94	iron 26 **Fe** 55.85	cobalt 27 **Co** 58.93	nickel 28 **Ni** 58.69	copper 29 **Cu** 63.55	zinc 30 **Zn** 65.41	gallium 31 **Ga** 69.72	germanium 32 **Ge** 72.64	arsenic 33 **As** 74.92	selenium 34 **Se** 78.96	bromine 35 **Br** 79.91	krypton 36 **Kr** 83.80
rubidium 37 **Rb** 82.47	strontium 38 **Sr** 87.62	yttrium 39 **Y** 88.91	zirconium 40 **Zr** 91.22	niobium 41 **Nb** 92.91	molybdenum 42 **Mo** 95.94	technetium 43 **Tc** 98	ruthenium 44 **Ru** 101.07	rhodium 45 **Rh** 102.91	palladium 46 **Pd** 106.42	silver 47 **Ag** 107.87	cadmium 48 **Cd** 112.41	indium 49 **In** 114.82	tin 50 **Sn** 118.71	antimony 51 **Sb** 121.76	tellurium 52 **Te** 127.6	iodine 53 **I** 126.90	xenon 54 **Xe** 131.29
cesium 55 **Cs** 132.91	barium 56 **Ba** 137.34	lutetium 71 **Lu** 174.97	hafnium 72 **Hf** 178.49	tantalum 73 **Ta** 180.94	tungsten 74 **W** 183.84	rhenium 75 **Re** 186.21	osmium 76 **Os** 190.23	iridium 77 **Ir** 192.22	platinum 78 **Pt** 195.08	gold 79 **Au** 196.97	mercury 80 **Hg** 200.59	thallium 81 **Tl** 204.38	lead 82 **Pb** 207.19	bismuth 83 **Bi** 208.98	polonium 84 **Po** 209	astatine 85 **At** 210	radon 86 **Rn** 222
francium 87 **Fr** 223	radium 88 **Ra** 226.03	lawrencium 103 **Lr** 262	rutherfordium 104 **Rf** 261	dubnium 105 **Db** 262	seaborgium 106 **Sg** 266	bohrium 107 **Bh** 264	hassium 108 **Hs** 269	meitnerium 109 **Mt** 268	ununnilium 110 **Uun** 271	unununium 111 **Uuu** 272	ununbium 112 **Uub** 285	ununtrium 113	ununquadium 114 **Uuq** 289		ununhexium 116 **Uuh** ?		ununoctium 118 **Uuo** ?

lanthanum 57 **La** 138.91	cerium 58 **Ce** 140.11	praseodymium 59 **Pr** 140.91	neodymium 60 **Nd** 144.24	promethium 61 **Pm** 146.92	samarium 62 **Sm** 150.36	europium 63 **Eu** 151.96	gadolinium 64 **Gd** 157.25	terbium 65 **Tb** 158.92	dysprosium 66 **Dy** 162.50	holmium 67 **Ho** 164.93	erbium 68 **Er** 167.26	thulium 69 **Tm** 168.93	ytterbium 70 **Yb** 173.04
actinium 89 **Ac** 227	thorium 90 **Th** 232.04	protactinium 91 **Pa** 231.04	uranium 92 **U** 238.03	neptunium 93 **Np** 237	plutonium 94 **Pu** 244	americium 95 **Am** 243	curium 96 **Cm** 247	berkelium 97 **Bk** 247	californium 98 **Cf** 251	einsteinium 99 **Es** 252	fermium 100 **Fm** 257	mendelevium 101 **Md** 258	nobelium 102 **No** 259

Name   Date

Matter Unit Review

Periodic Table

Read each question. Use the space provided to write or draw your answers.

1.   A beryllium atom has four protons and five neutrons. In the space provided, draw a model of
     a beryllium atom using the balls shown to represent the particles. You may refer to lessons to
     refresh your memory on how to draw an atom model.

   ◯   Electron

   ◯   Proton

   ⚫   Neutron

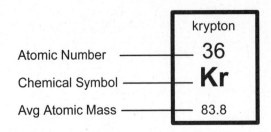

2. The atomic number is the number of protons in an atom of an element. In this example, the atomic number for krypton is 36. This tells us that an atom of krypton has 36 protons in its nucleus. The atomic mass is the number of protons plus the number of neutrons (protons + neutrons = atomic mass). If you know that the number of protons is 36 and the number of neutrons is 48, you can find atomic mass by adding the number of protons and neutrons, which equals 84.

    What is the atomic number and atomic mass of each atom listed in the table below?

Atom	Atomic Number	Atomic Mass
A neon atom has 10 protons and 10 neutrons.		
A potassium atom has 19 protons and 20 neutrons.		
A silver atom has 47 protons and 61 neutrons.		

3. You will need a copy of the Periodic Table of Elements to complete this question. The periodic table provides a lot of helpful information about each element. It provides the atomic number, chemical symbol, and the atomic mass. Remember, to find the number of neutrons you must subtract the number of protons from the atomic mass. Therefore, in the example, krypton has 48 neutrons (84 − 36 = 48).

    Use the periodic table to find the atomic number, atomic mass, number of protons, and number of neutrons of the elements listed in the table below.

Atom	Atomic Number	Atomic Mass	Number of Protons	Number of Neutrons
Hydrogen (H)				
Oxygen (O)				
Sodium (Na)				

The periodic table is organized in a logical manner. It's divided into groups and periods. Within these groups and periods are four main types of elements: noble gases, metals, nonmetals and metalloids. Each of these is defined below.

Groups – 8 vertical columns (not counting the 10 lower middle columns)

Periods – 7 horizontal rows

Noble Gases - The noble gases make up the group VIIIA, which is the last column in the periodic table. The noble gases fulfill the rule of having a full outer level with 8 valence electrons. Therefore, they do not undergo chemical reactions because they do not accept any electrons.

Metals - They easily lose electrons.

Nonmetals - They tend to gain electrons.

Metalloids - They have characteristics of metals and nonmetals.

4. Refer to the periodic table to answer the questions about the five elements listed below.

   Scandium (Sc)

   Copper (Cu)

   Gold (Au)

   Nitrogen (N)

   Krypton (Kr)

Which of these elements is/are metal(s)? _____

Which of these elements is/are classified as nonmetal(s)?_____

Which of these elements is/are noble gas(es)?_____

Which of these elements are in the same group? _____

Which of these elements are in the same period? _____

5. Use the list of words below to complete the blanks in the sentences. Some words may be used more than once.

   atom

   compound

   element

   molecule

All molecules contain more than one _____ .

Materials made of only one kind of atom are called_____.

All _____ and all _____ have chemical bonds.

Materials made of more than one element are called_____ .

Properties of Matter

6. Look at each property. Decide whether it is a chemical property or a physical property and place a check mark (✓) in the correct box next to the property.

Property	Chemical	Physical
freezing point		
flammability		
ability to rust		
hardness		
solubility		
malleability		
density		

7. Read the story below. Show whether a chemical change or a physical change is taking place during each event (in bold) by writing a C after the chemical changes and a P after the physical changes.

Serena **fried** _____ two eggs for her breakfast while she was waiting for the water to **boil**_____

for her tea. Butter **melted**_____as she spread it on her toast. After breakfast, she sat drinking

her tea and **digesting** _____her meal as she looked out the window at the **frost**_____that had

settled on the lawn overnight. Fall was coming, and soon the smell of **burning**_____ leaves

and **rotting** _____ jack-o'-lanterns would be in the air.

States of Matter

8. Answer these questions by writing *solid*, *liquid*, or *gas* in the blank spaces.

Rank the speed of particle motion in the three states of matter.

fastest _____

intermediate _____

slowest _____

Of the three states of matter, particles are farthest apart in a _____.

Particles cannot change positions in a _____.

The state of matter with a fixed volume but no fixed shape is _____.

Student Guide
Lesson 12: Unit Assessment

Lesson Objectives

- Distinguish between physical changes and chemical changes.
- Describe the structure of an atom, of an element, and its isotopes.
- Describe the patterns of organization represented in the periodic table.

PREPARE

Approximate lesson time is 60 minutes.

ASSESS

Unit Assessment: Matter (*Online*)

You will complete an online assessment of the main objectives covered so far in this unit. Follow the instructions online. Your assessment will be scored by the computer.

Student Guide
Lesson 1: Chemical Bonding

How would you describe this piece of matter? Is it spherical? Cubical? What properties might it have? The atoms that make up matter give it certain properties. In this case, the atoms that make up this grain of salt give the salt its properties. In this unit, we will explore how different types of atoms combine to form different types of substances. When different atoms join, the substances formed are compounds. Compounds have different properties, depending on their atoms.

Lesson Objectives

- Explain how compounds are formed by combining two or more different elements.
- Recognize that the properties of compounds differ from their constituent elements and provide examples.
- Describe how the arrangement of electrons affects the formation of ionic and covalent compounds.

PREPARE

Approximate lesson time is 60 minutes.

Materials

For the Student

🖳 Chemical Bonding Review

Keywords and Pronunciation

covalent bond (koh-VAY-luhnt) : a bond in which electrons are shared between the bonded atoms

ionic bond (iy-AH-nihk) : the force of attraction between a charged atom (or group of connected atoms) and another with the opposite charge

valence electrons (VAY-luhnts) : the electrons in the outermost shell of an atom

LEARN
Activity 1: Chemical Bonding *(Online)*

Activity 2: Chemical Bonding *(Online)*

ASSESS

Lesson Assessment: Chemical Bonding (*Online*)

You will complete an online assessment covering the main objectives of this lesson. Your assessment will be scored by the computer.

Name _____   Date _____

Chemical Bonding Review

Match the keyword to the correct definition. Write the keyword on the line after the definition.

ionic bond

covalent bond

valence electrons

1. the electrons in the outermost shell of an atom _____

2. a bond formed when oppositely charged ions attract_____

3. a bond formed when atoms share one or more pairs of electrons to get eight electrons
    in their valence shell _____

True or False?

4. NaCl is an atom of sodium (Na) and an atom of chlorine (Cl) that have combined by sodium
    capturing one electron from chlorine. _____

5. Two atoms of hydrogen must share their electrons to form H_2, a molecule with 2 electrons that
    are shared. _____

6. Water (H_2O) and hydrogen peroxide (H_2O_2) are both formed from compounds of hydrogen and
    oxygen. _____

7. An ionic bond means that electrons are transferred between atoms to create stable
    electron arrangements. A covalent bond means that a pair of electrons is being shared
    between atoms.

    _____

Student Guide
Lesson 2: Chemical Reactions

Have you ever seen or lived in a house that uses propane instead of natural gas or oil? People who live in rural areas often heat their homes and fuel their stoves with propane. Propane reacts with oxygen to produce heat, carbon dioxide, and water. Keep reading to find out how bonds are broken and new bonds are formed in this simple chemical reaction.

Lesson Objectives

- Explain how reactants enter into chemical reactions that result in products.
- Describe how chemical reactions involve breaking and reforming bonds (either ionic or covalent).
- Explain that energy is always involved in chemical reactions either as absorption or release of heat.
- Recognize that chemical reactions may involve the formation of a precipitate, the generation of gas, or a change in color.

PREPARE

Approximate lesson time is 60 minutes.

Keywords and Pronunciation

combustion reaction : an exothermic reaction in which oxides are usually formed

decomposition reaction : a kind of chemical reaction in which a single compound is broken down into two or more simpler compounds

endothermic reaction : a chemical reaction in which energy is absorbed from its surroundings

exothermic reaction : a chemical reaction in which energy is released to its surroundings

precipitate (prih-SIH-puh-tayt) : A solid that forms as a result of a chemical reaction. A white solid precipitate may form when aluminum chloride is added to a substance that contains aluminum.

products : the molecules that result from a chemical reaction

reactants : the starting molecules in a chemical reaction

LEARN
Activity 1: Chemical Reaction *(Online)*

Activity 2: Lesson *(Online)*

Instructions

Choose one of the following terms to best fit the definitions in Questions 1 to 6.

reactant

product

endothermic

exothermic

decomposition reaction

combustion reaction

1. The compounds that are produced in a chemical reaction are called

_____.

2. A chemical reaction that produces energy is called a(n)

_____.

3. A chemical reaction that involves the breakdown of reactants is called a(n)

_____.

4. A chemical reaction that requires energy is called a(n)

_____.

5. A type of chemical reaction that usually produces an oxide is called a(n)

_____.

6. The compounds that react in a chemical reaction are called

_____.

Complete the following telling whether the mixing of two chemicals was a chemical reaction. Write "indicates a chemical reaction" or "does not indicate a chemical reaction."

7. Rotten egg odor was detected.

_____

8. Purple color was observed when a red solution and a blue solution were mixed.

_____

9. Blue precipitate was observed.

_____

10. A green color was observed when colorless solutions were mixed.

_____

ASSESS

Lesson Assessment: Chemical Reactions (*Online*)

You will complete an online assessment covering the main objectives of this lesson. Your assessment will be scored by the computer.

Physical Science | Unit 3 : Chemistry | Lesson 3

Student Guide
Lesson 3: Chemical Formulas

If you were to pour hydrogen peroxide into one beaker and water into another beaker, you'd notice that the liquids look very much alike. But what you'd learn is that they react differently with different substances. They are both compounds that are composed of atoms of hydrogen and oxygen joined together to form molecules. So why do they have different properties? Soon you will be able to answer this question.

Lesson Objectives

- Compare ionic and covalent compounds and their molecular formulas.
- Identify various compounds by their chemical formulas.
- Explain and give examples of how chemical formulas can express chemical reactions.

PREPARE

Approximate lesson time is 60 minutes.

Keywords and Pronunciation

covalent bond (koh-VAY-luhnt) : a bond in which electrons are shared between the bonded atoms

covalent compound : any compound resulting from covalent bonding

ionic bond (iy-AH-nihk) : the force of attraction between a charged atom (or group of connected atoms) and another with the opposite charge

ionic compound : any compound resulting from ionic bonding

polymer (PAH-luh-muhr) : a molecule consisting of repeating chemical units

LEARN
Activity 1: Writing Chemical Formulas (Online)

Activity 2: Chemical Formulas (Online)
Instructions

Review what you have learned about the content of this lesson. When finished, place your completed lesson review sheet in your Science Notebook.

Write the chemical formula for each compound.

1. calcium oxide _____
2. potassium sulfide _____
3. magnesium chloride _____
4. aluminum oxide_____
5. magnesium fluoride _____

Identify the composition of each of the following. O2 Sample answer: 2 oxygen atoms

6. Na2SO4 _____
7. C6H8O6 _____
8. C6H12O6 _____
9. C3H5N3O9 _____

© 2013 K12 Inc. All rights reserved.
Copying or distributing without K12's written consent is prohibited.

97

Identify each of the following as an ionic compound or a covalent compound. Consult the periodic table to identify an element as a metal or nonmetal.

10. CH4 _____

11. H2S _____

12. CuF _____

13. PH3 _____

14. SrCl2 _____

Fill in the missing element and its subscript so the number of atoms on both sides of the arrow is the same.

15. 2 Fe + [ ] → 2 FeO

16. C + 2 [   ] → CH4

17. P4 + 6 H2 → 4 P[   ]

ASSESS

Lesson Assessment: Chemical Formulas, Part 1 (*Online*)

You will complete an online assessment covering the main objectives of this lesson. Your assessment will be scored by the computer.

Lesson Assessment: Chemical Formulas, Part 2 (*Offline*)

You will complete an offline assessment covering the main objectives of this lesson. Your learning coach will score this assessment.

Name _____   Date _____

Periodic Table of Elements

Element	Atomic Number	Symbol	Atomic Mass
hydrogen	1	H	1.01
helium	2	He	4.00
lithium	3	Li	6.94
beryllium	4	Be	9.01
boron	5	B	10.81
carbon	6	C	12.01
nitrogen	7	N	14.01
oxygen	8	O	15.99
fluorine	9	F	18.99
neon	10	Ne	20.18
sodium	11	Na	22.99
magnesium	12	Mg	24.31
aluminum	13	Al	26.98
silicon	14	Si	28.09
phosphorus	15	P	30.97
sulfur	16	S	32.07
chlorine	17	Cl	35.45
argon	18	Ar	39.95
potassium	19	K	39.10
calcium	20	Ca	40.08
scandium	21	Sc	44.96
titanium	22	Ti	47.87
vanadium	23	V	50.94
chromium	24	Cr	51.99
manganese	25	Mn	54.94
iron	26	Fe	55.85
cobalt	27	Co	58.93
nickel	28	Ni	58.69
copper	29	Cu	63.55
zinc	30	Zn	65.41
gallium	31	Ga	69.72
germanium	32	Ge	72.64
arsenic	33	As	74.92
selenium	34	Se	78.96
bromine	35	Br	79.91
krypton	36	Kr	83.80
rubidium	37	Rb	82.47
strontium	38	Sr	87.62
yttrium	39	Y	88.91
zirconium	40	Zr	91.22
niobium	41	Nb	92.91
molybdenum	42	Mo	95.94
technetium	43	Tc	98
ruthenium	44	Ru	101.07
rhodium	45	Rh	102.91
palladium	46	Pd	106.42
silver	47	Ag	107.87
cadmium	48	Cd	112.41
indium	49	In	114.82
tin	50	Sn	118.71
antimony	51	Sb	121.76
tellurium	52	Te	127.6
iodine	53	I	126.90
xenon	54	Xe	131.29
cesium	55	Cs	132.91
barium	56	Ba	137.34
lutetium	71	Lu	174.97
hafnium	72	Hf	178.49
tantalum	73	Ta	180.94
tungsten	74	W	183.84
rhenium	75	Re	186.21
osmium	76	Os	190.23
iridium	77	Ir	192.22
platinum	78	Pt	195.08
gold	79	Au	196.97
mercury	80	Hg	200.59
thallium	81	Tl	204.38
lead	82	Pb	207.19
bismuth	83	Bi	208.98
polonium	84	Po	209
astatine	85	At	210
radon	86	Rn	222
francium	87	Fr	223
radium	88	Ra	226.03
lawrencium	103	Lr	262
rutherfordium	104	Rf	261
dubnium	105	Db	262
seaborgium	106	Sg	266
bohrium	107	Bh	264
hassium	108	Hs	269
meitnerium	109	Mt	268
ununnilium	110	Uun	271
unununium	111	Uuu	272
ununbium	112	Uub	285
ununquadium	114	Uuq	289
ununhexium	116	Uuh	?
ununoctium	118	Uuo	?

Lanthanide series:

Element	Atomic Number	Symbol	Atomic Mass
lanthanum	57	La	138.91
cerium	58	Ce	140.11
praseodymium	59	Pr	140.91
neodymium	60	Nd	144.24
promethium	61	Pm	146.92
samarium	62	Sm	150.36
europium	63	Eu	151.96
gadolinium	64	Gd	157.25
terbium	65	Tb	158.92
dysprosium	66	Dy	162.50
holmium	67	Ho	164.93
erbium	68	Er	167.26
thulium	69	Tm	168.93
ytterbium	70	Yb	173.04

Actinide series:

Element	Atomic Number	Symbol	Atomic Mass
actinium	89	Ac	227
thorium	90	Th	232.04
protactinium	91	Pa	231.04
uranium	92	U	238.03
neptunium	93	Np	237
plutonium	94	Pu	244
americium	95	Am	243
curium	96	Cm	247
berkelium	97	Bk	247
californium	98	Cf	251
einsteinium	99	Es	252
fermium	100	Fm	257
mendelevium	101	Md	258
nobelium	102	No	259

Name _____   Date _____

Chemical Formulas Lesson Assessment

You are asked to teach a lesson on ionic and covalent compounds. Explain how you would:

1. Compare an ionic bond to a covalent bond.

    _____

    _____

    _____

2. Write the formula for an ionic compound.

    _____

    _____

    _____

3. Given chemical formulas, identify ionic compounds and covalent compounds.

    _____

    _____

    _____

    _____

    _____

4. Identify the difference between a molecular formula and a structural formula

    _____

    _____

Student Guide
Lesson 4: Lab: Testing and Producing Gases

Lesson Objectives

- Explain that reactions occur at different rates and that reaction rates can change.

PREPARE

Approximate lesson time is 60 minutes.

Advance Preparation

- If you don't already have it, you will need hydrogen peroxide (3%) and myriatic acid (diluted) for the Testing and Producing Gases activity.

- Perform all parts of the activity in a well-ventilated area.

- Have a sink accessible. All remaining solutions will be washed down the sink with lots of water.

Materials

For the Student

    🖥 Lab: Testing and Producing Gases

    hydrogen peroxide (3%)

    nail, galvanized

    safety glasses

    yeast

    candle

    gloves - protective

    graduated cylinder

    jar, with lid - 2

    matches - or lighter

    muriatic acid, diluted

    toothpicks

LEARN
Activity 1: Testing and Producing Gases *(Online)*

Safety

ASSESS

Lesson Assessment: Lab: Testing and Producing Gases (*Online*)

Have an adult review your answers to the Lab: Testing and Producing Gases, and input the results online.

Name _____   Date _____

Testing and Producing Gases

Goal

The goal of this activity is to produce several different gases through chemical reactions and to gain information about the identity of these gases using a lighted splint test.

Introduction

A chemical reaction occurs when substances known as reactants react to produce substances known as products, which have different chemical properties. There are many different types of chemical reactions. In this lab, you will have a chance to observe some of them. Remember that there are many clues indicating when a chemical reaction takes place. These clues include the production of a gas or solid, the release of light and heat, or a change in color.

Safety

- An adult should supervise this activity because the student will be working with acid, matches, and a flame.
- Some of the chemicals in this lesson, such as muriatic acid, are caustic or dangerous to handle. Be sure you have gloves and safety goggles on at all times. Wear long sleeves and long pants to protect your skin against splashes. If you spill the chemicals, call an adult to help you clean up. Perform all parts of the activity in an area that is well-ventilated, such as next to an open window. Wash all remaining solutions down the sink with lots of water.

Materials

2 small glass jars, with lids

hydrogen peroxide (3% solution)

muriatic acid, diluted

yeast

galvanized nail

toothpicks

candle

matches or lighter

eyedropper

graduated cylinder

safety goggles

protective gloves

Name   Date

Procedure

Part 1

1. Using a graduated cylinder, measure 70 mL of water. Pour this water into a small, empty glass jar. Dry the graduated cylinder.

2. Remember the old saying: "Do like you 'oughter'—add the acid to the water." This means to add acid to water—never the other way around. Do not add water to acid.

3. Make sure you are working in a well-ventilated area, such as next to an open window. Using extreme caution, and wearing safety goggles or protective eyeware, protective gloves, and long sleeves and long pants, measure out 30 mL of the muriatic acid into the graduated cylinder. Slowly pour this acid into the jar of water. (Add the acid carefully, because heat will be produced when the two substances mix.)

4. Screw the lid onto the jar and gently swirl the jar to mix the contents fully.

5. Remove the lid and place the galvanized nail into the jar.

6. Loosely cover the jar with the lid (do not screw it on).

7. Allow the reaction in the jar to continue for 20 seconds, recording observations during this time.

8. Light the wooden splint (toothpick) with the candle and prepare to test for the gas.

Testing and Producing Gases

9. Very carefully, remove the lid from the jar and bring the burning splint to the mouth of the jar.

10. Be prepared for a reaction. Record your observations.

11. Place the lid back on the jar and allow more gas to accumulate.

12. Complete Steps 7, 8, and 9 again to repeat this trial. After your second trial, rinse and dry the graduated cylinder to prepare for Part 2.

Part 2

13. Measure 50 mL of hydrogen peroxide using the graduated cylinder. Pour the hydrogen peroxide into the second jar.

14. Add approximately 1 teaspoon of yeast to the hydrogen peroxide. Loosely cover the jar with the lid (do not screw it on). Record your observations.

15. Light the wooden splint (toothpick) with the candle and allow the toothpick to burn for a few seconds.

16. Extinguish the flame by blowing on it so that the wood is just glowing.

17. Remove the lid on the jar and hold the glowing splint to the mouth of the jar. Record your observations.

18. Place the lid back on the jar and allow more gas to accumulate.

19. Repeat Steps 14 and 15 to complete a second trial

Name _____   Date _____

Safety

- Dispose of nail by taking it out of the acid solution (with gloves on), wrapping it in a paper towel, and putting it into the trash.

- Dispose of liquid substances by pouring them down a drain. Run plenty of cold water while you pour these substances down the drain and for several minutes afterward.

- Do not breathe in fumes. Make sure the area you are working in is well ventilated.

- Be sure toothpicks are completely extinguished in water before disposing of them.

Data and Observations

Observations for Part 1

Trial 1:

_____

_____

_____

Trial 2:

_____

_____

_____

Observations for Part 2

Trial 1:

_____

_____

_____

Trial 2:

_____

_____

_____

Name   Date
_____   _____

Analysis

1. Do you think a chemical reaction took place in Part 1 when you added the galvanized nail to
    the acid and water, and in Part 2 when the yeast was added to the hydrogen peroxide? Explain
    your answer.

    _____

    _____

    _____

2. Did the same result occur in both parts when you held up a lighted splint to the jar's mouth?
    What can you conclude from this about the identity of the gas(es) in Parts 1 and 2?

    _____

    _____

    _____

3. In both parts of the activity, you conducted a second trial without having to remix the
    chemicals. How was this possible?

    _____

    _____

    _____

4. In 1937, a large passenger airship called the Hindenburg mysteriously caught fire. Because
    the airship was filled with hydrogen gas, it immediately exploded once the fire reached the gas.
    Given this information, do you think one of the reactions above may have produced hydrogen?
    Use your data to explain your answer.

    _____

    _____

    _____

Name _____   Date _____

Testing and Producing Gases

Conclusions

Keeping the goal in mind, write a one- or two-sentence conclusion that summarizes the results of this activity and how they met the established goal.

_____

_____

_____

Student Guide
Lesson 5: Rates of Chemical Reactions

Lesson Objectives
- Explain that chemical reactions occur at different rates.
- Describe factors that influence the rate of reactions (e.g., changing the concentration of reactants, changing the surface area of solids, or using a catalyst).
- Provide examples that illustrate different reaction rates.

PREPARE

Approximate lesson time is 60 minutes.

Advance Preparation
- If you don't have it already, you will need wax paper, clear plastic cups, and antacid tablets (effervescent) for the Rates of Chemical Reactions lesson.

Materials
For the Student

🖥 Lesson Review

🖥 Can You Double the Bubbles?

stopwatch

antacid tablets, effervescent - 6

cups, clear plastic - 9 oz. recommended 6 (6)

graduated cylinder

pencil

spoon

thermometer

water - room temperature water for part 1; hot, warm, and cold water for part 2

wax paper - pieces - 2

Keywords and Pronunciation
catalyst (KA-tl-uhst) : a substance present during a chemical reaction that speeds up the reaction but is not used up or changed during the reaction

equilibrium : that state of chemical system in which the rates of the forward and reverse reactions are equal

reaction rate : how quickly a specific chemical reaction occurs under specific conditions over time

LEARN
Activity 1: Explore Rates of Chemical Reactions *(Online)*

Activity 2: Lesson Review *(Online)*

Activity 3: Can You Double the Bubbles? *(Online)*

ASSESS
Lesson Assessment: Rates of Chemical Reactions (*Online*)

You will complete an online assessment covering the main objectives of this lesson. Your assessment will be scored by the computer.

Name _____   Date _____

Rates of Chemical Reactions Review

Choose the best word to fit the definition.

reaction rate

catalyst

equilibrium

1. the state of a chemical system in which the forward and reverse reactions are equal

    _____

2. the speed of a reaction

    _____

3. a substance that speeds up a chemical reaction, but is not used up during it

    _____

4. How could you interpret the graph below?

    _____

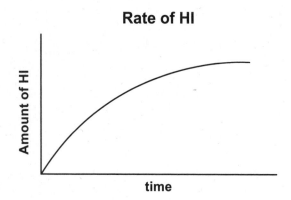

Rate of HI

Amount of HI

time

Name _____   Date _____

Can You Double the Bubbles?

Materials

Part I – Surface Area

thermometer

stopwatch

graduated cylinder

pencil

3 clear plastic cups (9 oz)

2 small pieces of waxed paper

3 effervescent antacid tablets

water (room temperature)

spoon

Part II – Temperature

thermometer

stopwatch

graduated cylinder

pencil

3 clear plastic cups (9 oz)

(You can reuse the cups from Part I; be sure to rinse them between Part I and Part II of the activity.)

3 effervescent antacid tablets

water (hot, cold, and room temperature)

Introduction

Effervescent antacid tablets contain sodium bicarbonate, which reacts with water to form carbon dioxide. In this activity, you will explore some influences that can affect the rate of this reaction, such as surface area and temperature.

Procedure

Before beginning, make sure you know how to use the stopwatch.

Name _____   Date _____

Part I – Surface Area

1. Using the graduated cylinder, fill 3 plastic cups each with 200 mL of room temperature water. Label the cups A, B, and C, respectively.

2. Measure the temperature of the water using the thermometer and record it on Data Table 1 (be sure to include the units). Each cup should have water at the same temperature, so you should only need to measure once.

3. Place one full antacid tablet in cup A and time how long it takes the tablet to dissolve. Start the stopwatch when you place the tablet in the water and stop it when you do not see any more of the tablet.

4. In Data Table 1, record how long it took to dissolve one full tablet.

5. Break a second antacid tablet into 4 pieces. Do this over a small piece of waxed paper so that you do not lose any pieces.

6. Place all 4 pieces (and any crumbs) of the antacid tablet into cup B and measure how long it takes to dissolve completely.

7. In Data Table 1, record how long it took all the pieces to dissolve.

8. Take the third tablet and crush it with the back of a spoon onto a piece of waxed paper. It should resemble a fine powder.

9. Place the entire crushed tablet into cup C and time how long it takes all of the pieces to dissolve.

10. In Data Table 1, record how long it took the crushed tablet to dissolve.

Data Table 1 – Surface Area

Temperature of water_____

Tablet Size	Dissolution Time (seconds)
Full tablet, cup A	
Tablet in 4 pieces, cup B	
Crushed tablet, cup C	

Name _____   Date _____

Questions

Part I – Surface Area (Refer to Data Table 1)

1. Which tablet dissolved the fastest? Why?

   _____
   _____
   _____

2. Why was it important that none of the pieces got lost when the tablet was broken or crumbled?

   _____
   _____
   _____

3. What variables other than the mass of the tablet were kept constant during this experiment?

   _____
   _____
   _____

Part II – Temperature

11. Gather 3 clean plastic cups and label them D, E, and F.

12. Fill cup D with 200 mL of room temperature water.

13. Measure the temperature of the water and record it in Data Table 2.

14. Place one full tablet in cup D and time how long it takes the tablet to dissolve. Record the result in Data Table 2.

15. Add 200 mL of very cold water to cup E.

16. Measure the temperature of the water and record it in Data Table 2.

17. Place one full tablet in cup E and time how long it takes the tablet to dissolve in the cold water. Record the result in Data Table 2.

18. Add 200 mL of hot water to cup F.

19. Measure the temperature of the water and record it in Data Table 2.

20. Place one full tablet in cup F and time how long it takes the tablet to dissolve in the hot water.

Record the result in Data Table 2.

Name _____   Date _____

Data Table 2 – Temperature

Water Temperature	Dissolution Time (seconds)
Cup D	
Cup E	
Cup F	

Questions

Part II – Temperature (Refer to Data Table 2)

1.   In which temperature water did the tablet dissolve the fastest? Why?

    _____

    _____

2.   Why was it important to use a whole tablet each time?

    _____

    _____

    _____

3.   What variables, other than the mass and surface area of the tablet, were kept constant during this experiment?

    _____

    _____

    _____

Student Guide
Lesson 6: Chemical Equations

Look at the reaction on-screen. What's happening? You can see that a solid is being added to a liquid. You see bubbles forming, which indicates a chemical reaction. In this reaction, vinegar, which is a liquid, and baking soda, which is a solid, combine to produce a gas. It might seem that some of the baking soda disappears, but nothing is lost in this reaction.

In this lesson, you'll learn how to balance chemical equations, showing that nothing is gained or lost in a chemical reaction.

Lesson Objectives

- Explain "conservation of mass" in chemical reactions.
- Describe a chemical reaction using a chemical equation.

PREPARE

Approximate lesson time is 60 minutes.

Materials

    For the Student

        🖳 A Balancing Act

        gumdrops

        marshmallows - option to gumdrops

        toothpicks

LEARN
Activity 1: Explore Chemical Equations *(Online)*

Activity 2: Chemical Equations *(Online)*
Instructions
Review what you have learned balancing chemical equations. When finished, place your completed lesson review sheet in your Science Notebook.

Answer the following questions.

1. Explain how the reaction below demonstrates the Law of Conservation of Mass.

    $Fe_2O_3 + 2Al \rightarrow 2Fe + Al_2O_3$

2. Explain how the reaction below violates the Law of Conservation of Mass. Then balance the equation.

    $H_2SO_4 + NaOH \rightarrow H_2O + Na_2SO_4$

3. Balance the following incomplete equations.

    a. $ZnS + O_2 \rightarrow ZnO + SO_2$

    b. $Fe_2O_3 + CO \rightarrow Fe + CO_2$

    c. $NH_3 + CuO \rightarrow N_2 + Cu + H_2O$

    d. $C_4H_{10} + O_2 \rightarrow CO_2 + H_2O$

4. What is the mass of one mole of the following? You will need a copy of the periodic table and a calculator.

   a. Cu
   b. Au
   c. H_2O
   d. C_4H_{12}

Activity 3: A Balancing Act *(Online)*

ASSESS

Lesson Assessment: Chemical Equations (*Online*)

You will complete an online assessment covering the main objectives of this lesson. Your assessment will be scored by the computer.

Name   Date

A Balancing Act

Materials

10 black gumdrops
24 green gumdrops
32 red gumdrops
toothpicks
Science Notebook
(colored marshmallows can also be used)

Introduction

In this activity, you will model balancing chemical equations using gumdrops to represent atoms.

Be aware that the molecules you make in this activity do not represent the actual shapes of the molecules you model. Use the following key to keep track of the atoms.

carbon – black
hydrogen – green
oxygen – red

1. In your Science Notebook, write the chemical formulas for ethane (C_2H_6), oxygen (O_2), carbon dioxide (CO_2), and water (H_2O). You will model these formulas using gumdrops and toothpicks.

2. **Build 2 ethane molecules.**
   Use 2 black gumdrops to represent carbon atoms and 6 green gumdrops to represent hydrogen atoms. Link the 2 carbon atoms together with a toothpick to represent a bond between them. Use 6 more toothpicks to attach the hydrogen atoms so there are 3 green gumdrops attached to each of the black gumdrops. Make 2 of these.

3. **Build 7 oxygen molecules.**
   Use 2 red gumdrops to represent oxygen atoms with a toothpick holding them together to represent the bond between them. Make 7 of these.

4. **Build 6 carbon dioxide molecules.**
   Use 1 black gumdrop to represent the carbon atom and 2 red gumdrops for the oxygen atoms. With the carbon atom in the center, attach the oxygen atoms on either side of the black gumdrop with 2 toothpicks. Make 6 of these.

5. **Build water molecules.**
   Use 1 red gumdrop to represent oxygen and 2 green gumdrops for hydrogen. Just like the molecule of carbon dioxide, attach each hydrogen atom to either side of the oxygen atom using toothpicks as bonds. Make 6 of these.

6. **Create a chemical equation.**
   Arrange 1 of each molecule so you have the reactants (ethane and oxygen) on the left side and the products (carbon dioxide and water) on the right (you may choose to create quick labels for reactants and products and draw an arrow in the middle).

7. Write this equation, using chemical formulas for each molecule, in your Science Notebook.

8. Is the equation you have modeled with one of each molecule balanced? Count the number of each atom type (carbon, hydrogen, and oxygen) on each side of the equation and record this in your Science Notebook.

Name _____   Date _____

9.   Using your extra molecules, continue to add them, respectively, to either the reactant side or the product side until the number of each atom type is the same on both the reactant and product side. Every time you add a new molecule recount all atoms until reactants and products have the same number of each type. Remember that you cannot balance the equation with individual gumdrops or by placing a reactant on the product side or vice versa.

10. When you have balanced the equation, record the number of each atom type in your Science Notebook, along with the final balanced equation using coefficients and chemical formulas.

Questions

1.   How many ethane molecules were needed to balance the equation?

   _____

   _____

2.   How many carbon dioxide molecules did you need to balance the equation?

   _____

   _____

3.   How many water molecules did you need to balance the equation?

   _____

   _____

4.   Say you wanted to create 8 molecules of carbon dioxide. How many molecules of ethane would you need?

   _____

   _____

   _____

5.   Suppose you began with 20 ethane molecules. How many molecules of water can you produce, assuming you had as much oxygen as needed?

   _____

   _____

   _____

   _____

Name

Date

Periodic Table of Elements

hydrogen 1 **H** 1.01																	helium 2 **He** 4.00
lithium 3 **Li** 6.94	beryllium 4 **Be** 9.01											boron 5 **B** 10.81	carbon 6 **C** 12.01	nitrogen 7 **N** 14.01	oxygen 8 **O** 15.99	fluorine 9 **F** 18.99	neon 10 **Ne** 20.18
sodium 11 **Na** 22.99	magnesium 12 **Mg** 24.31											aluminum 13 **Al** 26.98	silicon 14 **Si** 28.09	phosphorus 15 **P** 30.97	sulfur 16 **S** 32.07	chlorine 17 **Cl** 35.45	argon 18 **Ar** 39.95
potassium 19 **K** 39.10	calcium 20 **Ca** 40.08	scandium 21 **Sc** 44.96	titanium 22 **Ti** 47.87	vanadium 23 **V** 50.94	chromium 24 **Cr** 51.99	manganese 25 **Mn** 54.94	iron 26 **Fe** 55.85	cobalt 27 **Co** 58.93	nickel 28 **Ni** 58.69	copper 29 **Cu** 63.55	zinc 30 **Zn** 65.41	gallium 31 **Ga** 69.72	germanium 32 **Ge** 72.64	arsenic 33 **As** 74.92	selenium 34 **Se** 78.96	bromine 35 **Br** 79.91	krypton 36 **Kr** 83.80
rubidium 37 **Rb** 82.47	strontium 38 **Sr** 87.62	yttrium 39 **Y** 88.91	zirconium 40 **Zr** 91.22	niobium 41 **Nb** 92.91	molybdenum 42 **Mo** 95.94	technetium 43 **Tc** 98	ruthenium 44 **Ru** 101.07	rhodium 45 **Rh** 102.91	palladium 46 **Pd** 106.42	silver 47 **Ag** 107.87	cadmium 48 **Cd** 112.41	indium 49 **In** 114.82	tin 50 **Sn** 118.71	antimony 51 **Sb** 121.76	tellurium 52 **Te** 127.6	iodine 53 **I** 126.90	xenon 54 **Xe** 131.29
cesium 55 **Cs** 132.91	barium 56 **Ba** 137.34	lutetium 71 **Lu** 174.97	hafnium 72 **Hf** 178.49	tantalum 73 **Ta** 180.94	tungsten 74 **W** 183.84	rhenium 75 **Re** 186.21	osmium 76 **Os** 190.23	iridium 77 **Ir** 192.22	platinum 78 **Pt** 195.08	gold 79 **Au** 196.97	mercury 80 **Hg** 200.59	thallium 81 **Tl** 204.38	lead 82 **Pb** 207.19	bismuth 83 **Bi** 208.98	polonium 84 **Po** 209	astatine 85 **At** 210	radon 86 **Rn** 222
francium 87 **Fr** 223	radium 88 **Ra** 226.03	lawrencium 103 **Lr** 262	rutherfordium 104 **Rf** 261	dubnium 105 **Db** 262	seaborgium 106 **Sg** 266	bohrium 107 **Bh** 264	hassium 108 **Hs** 269	meitnerium 109 **Mt** 268	ununnillium 110 **Uun** 271	unununium 111 **Uuu** 272	ununbium 112 **Uub** 285	ununquadium 114 **Uuq** 289		ununhexium 116 **Uuh** ?			ununoctium 118 **Uuo** ?

lanthanum 57 **La** 138.91	cerium 58 **Ce** 140.11	praseodymium 59 **Pr** 140.91	neodymium 60 **Nd** 144.24	promethium 61 **Pm** 146.92	samarium 62 **Sm** 150.36	europium 63 **Eu** 151.96	gadolinium 64 **Gd** 157.25	terbium 65 **Tb** 158.92	dysprosium 66 **Dy** 162.50	holmium 67 **Ho** 164.93	erbium 68 **Er** 167.26	thulium 69 **Tm** 168.93	ytterbium 70 **Yb** 173.04
actinium 89 **Ac** 227	thorium 90 **Th** 232.04	protactinium 91 **Pa** 231.04	uranium 92 **U** 238.03	neptunium 93 **Np** 237	plutonium 94 **Pu** 244	americium 95 **Am** 243	curium 96 **Cm** 247	berkelium 97 **Bk** 247	californium 98 **Cf** 251	einsteinium 99 **Es** 252	fermium 100 **Fm** 257	mendelevium 101 **Md** 258	nobelium 102 **No** 259

Student Guide
Lesson 8. Optional: Lab: Dissolving Metals

Lesson Objectives
- Draw conclusions based on the results of an investigation.
- Collect pertinent data from a scientific investigation to test a hypothesis or provide information.

PREPARE

Approximate lesson time is 60 minutes.

Advance Preparation
- If you don't have it already, you will need Root Eater (containing copper sulfate) or Bluestone Algicide (containing copper sulfate) for this optional lesson. Root Eater is found in garden stores. The material may be expensive and difficult to buy in small quantities.

Materials
For the Student

    🖳 Dissolving Metals Lab

        nail, galvanized

        aluminum foil

        copper wire

        cups, clear plastic - small (4)

        eyedropper

        gloves

        graduated cylinder

        plastic spoons

        root eater - or Bluestone Algicide, available at garden stores

        safety goggles

        water

LEARN
Activity 1. Optional: Dissolving Metal *(Online)*

ASSESS

Optional. Diagnostic Test: Lab: Dissolving Metals (*Online*)
Have an adult review your answers to the Lab: Dissolving Metals, and input the results online.

Name _____ Date _____

Dissolving Metals

Goal

The goal of this activity is to determine how three different metals—zinc, copper, and aluminum—react when they are immersed in a solution of copper sulfate (made from Root Eater).

Introduction

From your earlier activity with a galvanized nail and muriatic acid, you know that metals can react with some chemical solutions. But from your daily life, you also know that a quarter won't undergo a chemical reaction if it gets wet. So what determines whether a metal will react with a substance? What is produced when a chemical reaction takes place with a metal? In this activity, you will have a chance to test three different metals—zinc (from the outer covering of a galvanized nail), aluminum (from foil), and copper (from wire)—to determine how they react with a particular chemical solution, copper sulfate. As you complete this activity, keep in mind that chemical reactions only serve to rearrange the elements and atoms present in the reactants.

SAFETY

Some of the chemicals in this lesson are caustic or dangerous to handle.

Be sure you have gloves and safety goggles on at all times.

Wear long sleeves and long pants to avoid exposure to your skin due to splashing.

If you spill the chemicals, call an adult to help you clean up.

Perform the activity in a well-ventilated area, such as next to an open window.

Do not inhale the Root Eater powder.

Read the label on the Root Eater to find out how to dispose of the chemical. Do not pour any unused product down a drain or on the ground.

Wear closed-toe and closed-heel shoes.

Tie back long hair, and remove jewelry before beginning the lab.

Do not breathe dust.

Keep container closed.

Avoid contact with eyes and skin.

Wash thoroughly after handling.

If Root Eater comes in contact with eyes, immediately flush the eye with plenty of water.

If Root Eater comes in contact with skin, wash off with water.

If Root Eater is swallowed, wash out the mouth with plenty of water if the person is conscious and call for medical aid.

Materials

galvanized nail

small square of aluminum foil

small length of copper wire

4 small, clear plastic cups

Root Eater (from a garden store, contains copper sulfate pentahydrate)

plastic spoon

water, tap

graduated cylinder

eyedropper

safety goggles

protective gloves

Procedure

Note: Before you begin, put on your safety goggles and protective gloves. Remember to wear long sleeves and long pants while performing this activity.

1. Measure 20 mL of water, and pour it into one plastic cup. Mix a solution of copper sulfate by dissolving a pinch of Root Eater in the water. Mix carefully with a plastic spoon as needed.

2. In one plastic cup, place a galvanized nail. In the second plastic cup, place a small square of aluminum foil. In the third plastic cup, place the small section of copper wire. All three samples of metal should be of similar size.

3. Add approximately 10 drops of the copper sulfate solution to each of the three cups. Make sure to get the solution on the metal samples.

4. Allow several minutes to pass. Record your observations in the Data Table for each cup.

Data Table

Cup	Observations
Cup 1: galvanized nail	
Cup 2: aluminum foil	
Cup 3: copper wire	

Analysis

1. In which cups did a chemical reaction take place? Explain your answer.

_____

_____

_____

2. Did the galvanized nail in this activity behave similarly to the galvanized nail in Lesson 4, Testing and Producing Gases, when muriatic acid was added to it? Explain.

_____

_____

_____

3. Were any gases produced in the cups when the copper sulfate solution was added to them?

_____

4. What did you notice about the color of the copper sulfate solution before it was added to the metals and after? The color in the copper sulfate solution comes from the copper ions that are present. With this information, what substance would you speculate was formed in the reactions that took place?

_____

_____

5. With this information, what substance would you speculate was formed in the reactions that took place? (Hint: Remember that no new elements can be formed in a chemical reaction. Instead, all products must be formed from the elements that were present with the reactants.)

_____

_____

_____

Conclusion

Write a two- or three-sentence conclusion to summarize what this activity showed about how the different metals react with the copper sulfate solution.

_____

_____

_____

_____

Student Guide
Lesson 9: Mixtures

What exactly are those spicy green things in the party mix? If you don't like them, you can always pick them out, right? In fact, you could pull out any ingredient in the party mix and separate it from the others—the peanuts, the pretzel bits, or the cereal pieces. The pretzel bits would still be salty, like they were when they were mixed in with everything else. The cereal pieces would still be sweet and crunchy. Taking them out of the party mix doesn't change their physical properties.

This party mix is a **mixture**.

Lesson Objectives

- Explain that the properties of a substance or mixture depend on the properties, motions, and interaction of its molecules.
- Given a list of common substances and chemical formulas, classify matter as elements, compounds, or mixtures.
- Define homogeneous mixtures and heterogeneous mixtures, and recognize examples of each.

PREPARE

Approximate lesson time is 60 minutes.

Advance Preparation

- If you don't have it already, you will need borax for this lesson.

Materials

For the Student

🖳 Lesson Review

cups, plastic - disposable, 16 ounce (2)

measuring spoon - teaspoon

bags, plastic - sandwich size

borax - 1 tsp. This is found in the laundry detergent aisle of most supermarkets.

craft sticks - wooden (3)

food coloring

glue, white - approximately 1/4 cup

measuring cup

water

LEARN
Activity 1: Mixtures *(Online)*

Activity 2: Mixtures *(Online)*

Activity 3: Slime: Changing Properties *(Online)*
Instructions
Activity 3. Slime: Changing Properties (Offline)

Materials:

white glue (approximately 1/4 cup)

borax (1 tsp) (This is found in the laundry detergent aisle of most supermarkets.)

plastic bags, sandwich size

food coloring

plastic cups (2)

wooden craft sticks (3)

measuring cups and spoons

water

Science Notebook

Procedure

1. Measure ¼ cup of white glue and pour it into one of the disposable plastic cups.

2. Measure ¼ cup of water and pour it into the same cup with the glue.

3. Use a wooden craft stick to stir until the glue is mixed with the water. If you wish to color your slime, add a few drops of food coloring at this point and stir more.

4. In your Science Notebook, record any observations about the contents of the cup.

5. In a second plastic cup, measure a cup of water.

6. Add 1 teaspoon of borax to the cup with water. Use another craft stick to stir the solution until the borax dissolves in the water.

7. In your Science Notebook, record any observations about the contents of the cup.

8. Carefully pour the borax solution into the glue solution. Stir with another craft stick.

9. In your Science Notebook, record any observations about the contents of the cup.

If you want, you can remove the slime from the cup and feel it with your fingers. As you play with it, make a note of any changes you observe.

You can keep your slime in a plastic bag in the refrigerator for several days, if you wish.

Questions

Answer these questions.

1. This procedure actually formed a new compound, slime, from the original compounds of glue, borax, and water. Given this information, is slime a pure substance or a mixture?

----

2. Before you removed the slime from the cup, you may have noticed that the slime was "floating" in liquid. Were the contents of the cup a mixture or a compound? Explain your answer.

----

3. Does your final compound of slime have the properties the same as or different from those of the compounds used to make it? If different, give an example of a specific property that changed.

ASSESS

Lesson Assessment: Mixtures, Part 1 (*Online*)
You will complete an online assessment covering the main objectives of this lesson. Your assessment will be scored by the computer.

Lesson Assessment: Mixtures, Part 2 (*Offline*)
You will complete an offline assessment covering the main objectives of this lesson. Your learning coach will score this assessment.

Name _____   Date _____

Mixtures Review

1. Complete the chart below to describe how compounds and mixtures differ. One box has already been filled in for you.

Compound	Mixture
Components can be separated only by chemical means.	

2. What is the main difference between a homogeneous mixture and a heterogeneous mixture?

_____

_____

3. What is a solution? Give an example.

_____

_____

4. Identify each of the following as an element, a compound, or a mixture.

a) food coloring in water　　_____

b) tin　　　　　　　　　　_____

c) oxygen　　　　　　　　_____

d) water　　　　　　　　　_____

e) air　　　　　　　　　　_____

f) granola　　　　　　　　_____

g) sand　　　　　　　　　_____

Name _____ Date _____

Mixtures Lesson Assessment

Answer the following question.

10 pts.

1. Describe the saltwater in oceans. Explain whether it is a mixture or compound and how you would show this.

    _____

    _____

    _____

    _____

Student Guide
Lesson 10: Separating Mixtures

Have you ever heard the expression, "It was like finding a needle in a haystack"? It means that it was really difficult to find something. So, how could you go about finding a needle in a haystack? You could use a pair of tweezers to search through the straw in the haystack. Or, you could use a magnet to attract the metal needle, pulling it out of the haystack. You can probably think of other creative ways to find that needle, which represents one component in a mixture.

In this lesson, we will explore different ways of separating mixtures into their components, much like finding a needle in a haystack.

Lesson Objectives

- Explain how mixtures can be separated by physical methods, such as mixing, magnetic attraction, evaporation, filtration, distillation, chromatography, and settling.
- Interpret diagrams with examples of these methods of forming and separating mixtures.

PREPARE

Approximate lesson time is 60 minutes.

Materials

For the Student

🖳 Lesson Review

cups, plastic - tall (preferably clear) (2)

filter paper - Can use coffee filter

pencil (2)

rubbing alcohol

ruler, metric

tape

water

Keywords and Pronunciation

chromatography (kroh-muh-TAH-gruh-fee) : separation of substances in a mixture by differences in their attraction to a substance over which they are passed

distillation : physically separating a solution of a solid and a liquid by boiling off the liquid

LEARN
Activity 1: Separating Mixtures *(Online)*

Activity 2: Separating Mixtures (Online)

Activity 3: Chromatography (Online)
Instructions
Activity 3. Chromatography (Offline)

Materials
pencil (2)
ruler
tape
black ballpoint pen
filter paper (coffee filter)
tall plastic cup (2)
rubbing alcohol (isopropanol)
water
Procedure
1. Cut two strips of filter paper each about 2 cm wide. Cut them long enough to tape to a pencil and have it hang into the cup from the pencil (laid across the top of the cup) to reach about 1 cm from the bottom of the cup.
2. Draw a large dot on the filter paper with the black ballpoint pen about 2 cm from the bottom of the filter paper.
3. Pour alcohol into one cup to a depth of just under 2 cm. Pour water into the other cup to a depth of just under 2 cm.
4. Tape one filter paper strip to a pencil, with the dot from the black pen on the far side from the pencil. Repeat with the other filter paper strip and pencil.
5. Place one pencil across the top of the cup containing alcohol with the filter paper hanging down, so that the filter paper hangs into the cup and reaches the alcohol without the drawn dot getting into the alcohol (adjust the depth of the alcohol in the cup if necessary). Place the other pencil across the top of the cup containing water in the same way.
6. Watch for about 15 minutes while the alcohol or water absorbs into the paper, reaches the black dot, and moves up the paper.
7. When the alcohol line reaches about 1 cm from the pencil, remove the filter paper from the alcohol and observe what happened to the ink line.
8. Use what you observe to answer the questions.
Questions
1. What happened to the black dot that was exposed to rubbing alcohol?

----

2. What happened to the black dot that was exposed to water?

----

3. Based on what you have learned about chromatography, explain what happened in both liquids.

ASSESS

Lesson Assessment: Separating Mixtures (*Online*)

You will complete an online assessment covering the main objectives of this lesson. Your assessment will be scored by the computer.

Name _____   Date _____

Separating Mixtures Review

1. Identify the location of the solid salt and the pure water in the diagram below.

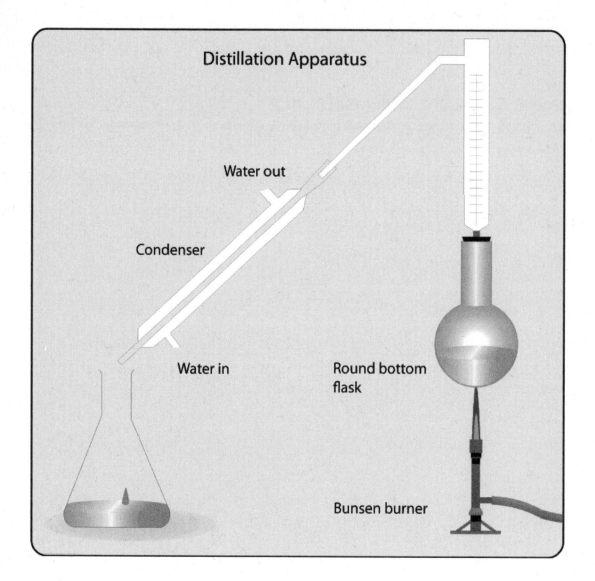

Distillation Apparatus

Water out

Condenser

Water in

Round bottom flask

Bunsen burner

2. For each mixture described below, suggest an appropriate method for separating the mixture. Explain your answer.

a. crude oil

_____

b. small pebbles and water

_____

c. paint pigments

_____

d. magnetite from quartz grains

_____

e. silt and water

_____

Student Guide
Lesson 11: Solutions

Lesson Objectives
- Define and differentiate solvent, solute, and solution.
- Interpret data presented in solubility graphs and explain the effect of different variables on solubility rates.

PREPARE

Approximate lesson time is 60 minutes.

Materials
For the Student

    🖳 Solutions Review

    🖳 Temperature and Solubility

    baking soda

    glasses, drinking (3)

    pan

    pot holder

    stopwatch

    Epsom salt

    salt, table

    spoon

    stove

    thermometer - Celsius

    towel

Keywords and Pronunciation

compound (KAHM-pownd) : A substance containing atoms of two or more elements. Water is a compound of hydrogen and oxygen.

heterogeneous mixture : a mixture in which different parts have different compositions, made of different proportions of particular atoms or molecules

homogeneous mixture : a mixture in which the ratio of each component to the others is the same everywhere in the mixture

mixture : A combination of two or more substances that do not change chemically when mixed. Trail mix is an example of a mixture.

saturated : dissolving the greatest possible amount of a substance in a solution.

solubility (sahl-yuh-BIH-luh-tee) : How much solute can be dissolved in a solvent at a given temperature. The solubility of the sugar increased when we raised the temperature.

solute (SAHL-yoot) : the minor constituent of a solution

solution : A mixture in which the substances are completely and evenly mixed, down to their individual molecules. Sugar-water is a solution.

---

solvent : the main constituent of a solution, or the one that provides a substance´s main physical property

substance : Matter that has particular properties. Salt is a substance that dissolves easily in water.

LEARN

Activity 1: Solutions *(Online)*

Activity 2: Solutions *(Online)*

Activity 3: Temperature and Solubility *(Online)*

ASSESS

Lesson Assessment: Solutions, Part 1 (*Online*)

You will complete an online assessment covering the main objectives of this lesson. Your assessment will be scored by the computer.

Lesson Assessment: Solutions, Part 2 (*Offline*)

You will complete an offline assessment covering the main objectives of this lesson. Your learning coach will score this assessment.

Name _____   Date _____

Solutions Review

It's almost time for bed, but before you're ready to go to sleep, you decide to make yourself a cup of hot chocolate and a tasty snack. As the milk is heating, you pour some pretzels, popcorn, and cereal bits into a big bowl. When the milk is hot, you stir in the hot chocolate mix, and settle down to enjoy your snack.

1. Which mixture is most likely homogeneous?

_____

2. Which mixture is most likely heterogeneous?

_____

3. Identify the solution in this story.

_____

4. Identify the solute in this story.

_____

5. Identify the solvent in this story.

_____

6. Do you think the chocolate would have mixed in with the milk more quickly if the milk had been cold? Explain your answer.

_____

_____

Name _____   Date _____

Temperature and Solubility

Materials:

12 tsp Epsom salt
12 tsp salt
12 tsp baking soda
3 glasses
towel
stopwatch
stovetop
pan
potholders
Celsius thermometer
spoon

Procedures:

1. In your Science Notebook, write a hypothesis stating what effect you think temperature will have on the dissolving rate of each of the three powders used in this experiment.

2. In a pan, heat 3 L of water to 58°C.

3. Using the potholders, carefully pour approximately 250 mL of the heated water into a glass.

4. Place 1 tsp of the Epsom salt into the water. Start the stopwatch as soon as you have poured the Epsom salt into the water. *Hint:You may wish to have someone else use the stopwatch for you.* Stir with a spoon to help the Epsom salt dissolve. When the Epsom salt has completely dissolved, stop the timer and record, on the Solubility Data Table, how long it took for the Epsom salt to dissolve.

5. Repeat Step 2 through 4 using the salt and baking soda.

6. Pour the water out of all three glasses and wash them thoroughly.

7. In a pan, heat 3 L of water to 70°C.

8. Repeat Steps 3 through 6 using the Epsom salt, salt, and baking soda. Be sure to record the dissolving time for each powder.

9. In a pan, heat 3 L of water to 100°C.

10. Repeat Steps 3 through 5 using the Epsom salt, salt, and baking soda. Be sure to record the dissolving time for each powder.

11. Study the dissolving times in your data table. Calculate the average dissolving time for each substance and record that information.

Name _____   Date _____

Solubility Data Table

Temperature	Epsom Salt Dissolving Time	Salt Dissolving Time	Baking Soda Dissolving Time	Average Dissolving Time
58°C				
70°C				
100°C				

Questions:

1. At which temperature did each powder dissolve the slowest?

   _____

2. At which temperature did each powder dissolve the fastest?

   _____

3. What was the average time that it took each powder to dissolve?

   • Epsom salt _____

   • Salt _____

   • Baking soda _____

4. Was your hypothesis correct? How do you know?

   _____

   _____

   _____

Name _____   Date _____

Solutions Assessment

Use the information on the solubility graph to answer Questions 1 – 3.

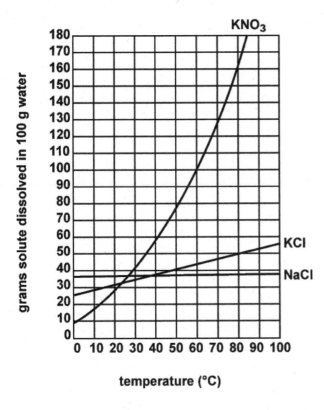

1. Which compound shows the smallest increase in solubility with increasing temperature? Is it KCl, NaCl, or KNO_3?

   _____

2. Which compound shows the greatest increase in solubility with increasing temperature? Is it KCl, NaCl, or KNO_3?

   _____

3. Explain the relationship between temperature and solubility as illustrated by the graph

   _____

   _____

Student Guide
Lesson 12: Substances

Lesson Objectives

- Compare mixtures and solutions.
- Given a list of common substances and/or chemical formulas, classify matter as elements, molecules, compounds, solutions, or mixtures

---

PREPARE

Approximate lesson time is 60 minutes.

Materials

For the Student

🖳 Substances Review

🖳 Which Mixture is Which?

powdered drink mix

sand

soap, liquid - clear

sugar - fine, granulated

cups, clear plastic (10)

flashlight

food coloring - 1 color

glue, white

pepper

plastic spoons

salt, table

spoon

water - tap

water, distilled - or bottled

LEARN
Activity 1: Substances *(Online)*

Activity 2: Substances *(Online)*

Activity 3: Which Mixture is Which? *(Online)*

ASSESS

Lesson Assessment: Substances (*Online*)

You will complete an online assessment covering the main objectives of this lesson. Your assessment will be scored by the computer.

Activity 3: Which Mixture is Which? *(Online)*

Name _____   Date _____

Substances Review

1. What is the difference between a homogeneous mixture and a heterogeneous mixture?

    _____

    _____

    _____

2. Classify each of these substances as either a *solution* or *heterogeneous mixture*:

    a. oil and vinegar salad dressing   _____

    b. red fruit drink   _____

    c. antifreeze   _____

    d. granite countertop   _____

3. Describe how the ingredients in a bottle of oil and vinegar salad dressing will look after you shake the bottle.

    _____

    _____

    _____

4. Describe how the oil and vinegar salad dressing from Question 3 will look after sitting on the countertop for about one hour after it was shaken.

    _____

    _____

5. Describe how the contents of a bottle of red fruit drink will look in the following situations: before shaking the bottle, directly after shaking the bottle, and one hour after the bottle was shaken.

    _____

    _____

Name _____   Date _____

Which Mixture is Which?

Materials

10 clear plastic or glass cups

plastic spoons

salt

pepper

bottled or distilled water

tap water

food coloring

powdered drink mix

white glue

sand

clear liquid soap

sugar, fine granulated

flashlight

spoon

Procedures

1. In your Science Notebook, create a data table with 11 rows and 3 columns. Label the first column Cup Number, label the second column Ingredients, and label the final column Mixture Type. Title the table, Mixture Identification Data Table. Label the cups 1 through 10.

2. For each mixture you make in this activity, record the cup number in column one and the ingredients used in column two. Then identify whether the mixture is heterogeneous or homogeneous and record your answer in the third column.

3. Place two spoonfuls of salt in cup 1 and add two spoonfuls of pepper. Mix them together.

4. Fill cup 2 with one cup of tap water.

5. Fill cup 3 with one cup of bottled water.

6. Fill cup 4 with one cup of bottled water, then add three or four drops of food coloring. Mix well.

7. Fill cup 5 with one cup of bottled water, then add two spoonfuls of salt. Mix well.

8. Fill cup 6 with one cup of bottled water, then add half a package of powdered drink mix. Mix well.

9. Fill cup 7 with one cup of bottled water, then add two spoonfuls of sand. Mix well.

10. Fill cup 8 with one cup of bottled water, then add two spoonfuls of sugar. Mix well.

11. Fill cup 9 with one cup of bottled water, then add one spoonful of the liquid soap. Mix gently (avoiding bubbles) for approximately two minutes.

12. Fill cup 10 with one cup of bottled water, then add one spoonful of glue. Mix.

13. Darken the room, if possible. Shine the flashlight into each of the liquid mixtures, or just hold the lighted flashlight against the side of each cup. Do you observe any particles that have not dissolved?

Questions

1. Which mixtures are homogeneous mixtures? How do you know?

_____

_____

_____

2. Which mixtures are heterogeneous mixtures? How do you know?

_____

_____

_____

3. Which of the mixtures can be separated by physical means? List at least four different ways in which this could generally be accomplished.

_____

_____

_____

_____

Student Guide
Lesson 13: Lab: Separating Ingredients

Lesson Objectives
- Investigate techniques for separating mixtures.

PREPARE

Approximate lesson time is 60 minutes.

Materials

For the Student

🖥 Separating Ingredients

cranberry juice - 16 oz.

pan - small

pot holder

aluminum foil (2)

broom handle

cups - paper (9)

diet soda - 16 oz.

duct tape

graduated cylinder - 100mL minimum

ice, crushed

jar, large glass - wide-mouth

jar, small - glass

marker, permanent

orange soda - 16 oz.

stove

LEARN
Activity 1: Lab: Separating Ingredients *(Online)*
Safety
During the Separating Ingredients lab, it's important to watch the boiling liquid closely and have an adult present at all times.

ASSESS

Lesson Assessment: Lab: Separating Ingredients (*Online*)

Have an adult review your answers to the Lab: Separating Ingredients, and input the results online.

Name _____   Date _____

Lab: Separating Ingredients

Goal

The goal of this lab is for students to separate some of the liquid from other ingredients of some common beverages by using a process known as distillation, and to compare the amounts of this distilled liquid among the different beverages.

Introduction

Have you ever wondered what makes fruit juices and colas so brightly colored? Or even what gives them their flavor? In fact, if you read the labels of many of these popular beverages, you might be surprised to see how many ingredients are used, including many artificial colors, flavorings, and sweeteners. In this activity, you will separate some of the liquid from other ingredients by taking advantage of their different boiling points. This process is known as distillation, and, although it can be conducted in a laboratory with sophisticated equipment, it can also be done with simple household items. In this process, you will be asked to heat a sample beverage and watch as a liquid is evaporated out of the beverage and then condensed into another container. Because the beverages used are mixtures of different ingredients, each with its own unique boiling point, the first liquid to evaporate and separate will be the ingredient with the lowest boiling point.

In this experiment, you will be taking two different types of observations, qualitative and quantitative. Qualitative data requires word descriptions, such as describing color, texture, bubbling, and so forth. Quantitative data requires numbers obtained by measuring or counting, such as using a ruler to measure length, using a graduated cylinder to measure volume, counting the number of objects that are a certain color, and so forth.

Materials

16 oz (474 mL) cranberry juice
16 oz (474 mL) diet cola
16 oz (474 mL) orange soda
graduated cylinder
small sauce pan
50-60 cm piece of aluminum foil
large glass jar
crushed ice
small glass jar (to fit easily into the larger jar)
broom handle
heat source (range top, stove, or alcohol burner)
empty pot
9 paper cups
permanent marker (to label paper cups)
duct tape
empty pot
hot mitt or pad

Lab: Separating Ingredients

Safety
Use extreme caution when the heat source is turned on. Be careful not to touch the aluminum foil condenser or the soda can once the heat source is on, as it will heat up rapidly and can cause burns.

Procedure
1. Wrap the aluminum foil lengthwise around the broom handle to create a long tube. Be sure to wrap the foil several times around so there is no open seam. Cover the seam with a long, narrow strip of duct tape so the tube is completely sealed along the side. Carefully slide the aluminum foil tube off the broom handle, being sure not to open the seams or crush the tube. This tube will serve as a condenser, which will allow steam to enter at the end of the tube attached to a container where the initial solution is heated. As it moves through the tube, the steam will transfer heat energy to the cooler wall of the tube, which in turn will transfer heat energy to the cooler surrounding air. As it loses its heat energy, the steam will condense into a liquid. This liquid will then run out the open end of the tube into a collection vessel.

2. Using the graduated cylinder, measure out 200 mL of the cranberry juice. Record this amount as your starting amount of liquid in the Data Table. In the space provided on the Data and Observations page, record observations of the properties of the liquid, including its color and its viscosity (thickness). Pour this quantity into the small sauce pan. (If the 200 mL of juice does not substantially cover the bottom of your sauce pan, measure a volume of juice that will do so and use this amount of liquid instead of 200 mL in all subsequent equivalent steps.

3. With the marking pen, label one paper cup Cranberry Juice. Pour 200 mL of the cranberry juice into this cup.

4. Fill the large jar approximately three-quarters full with crushed ice.

5. Fit the smaller jar into the large ice-filled jar so the small jar is surrounded by ice on the bottom and sides.

6. The key to success in this exercise is making the distillation apparatus. It's tricky, so be innovative. Put four squares of aluminum foil on top of another so that the edges lap over the edge of the sauce pan. Pick up all four pieces and lay them on a flat surface. Trace the circumference of the tube in the center of the squares. Using duct tape, tape around the circumference—then pierce the hole with a knife, insert the tube, and use more duct tape to make a good seal. Place this back over the small sauce pan and press it into place around the edges of the pan.

7. Place the sauce pan containing cranberry juice on the heat source. (You will turn the heat on in a later step.)

8. Position the small collection jar, now submerged in ice, so that the long side of the condenser rests inside the small jar. This final setup should allow any liquid that comes from the sauce pan to travel through the condenser and into the small collection jar.

9. Use small pieces of duct tape to tape the connection between the condenser and the collection jar to seal it as much as possible.

Lab: Separating Ingredients

10. Wrap some crushed ice in some aluminum foil (or a sandwich bag) so that no melting ice can escape. Place this ice on top of the collection jar and duct-tape seal. This will help the steam condense into water in the collection jar.

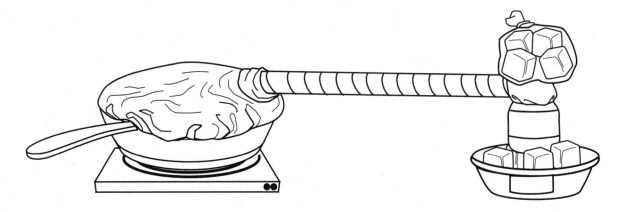

11. Turn the heat source to high and listen carefully for the juice inside the sauce pan to begin to boil.

12. Once you hear the boiling, begin timing and watch the end of the condenser in the collection jar. In the space provided on the Data and Observations page, record any properties or observations about the liquid that appear. Also, be sure to make a note of the rate at which the liquid appears. After 5 minutes of boiling, remove the pot from the heat source and place on a heat-proof surface.

13. Allow the sauce pan to cool for at least 5 minutes. Using a hot pad, pour the remaining liquid in the sauce pan into the graduated cylinder. Record the amount remaining in the Data Table.

14. Pour this liquid into a paper cup and label it Cranberry Juice – Remaining Liquid. Compare this sample to the paper cup labeled Cranberry Juice and record your observations.

15. Using a graduated cylinder, measure how much liquid you distilled into the collection jar. Record this measurement in the Data Table. Then pour the liquid into a paper cup, and label it Cranberry Juice—Distilled Liquid. Add any other observations you might have for this liquid, being sure to compare it to the liquid in the cup labeled Cranberry Juice.

16. Rinse the small jar and dry it well.

17. Repeat steps 2-19 twice more, once with the diet cola and once with the orange soda. Label the paper cups appropriately and fill in the correct parts of the Data Table and the Data and Observations page.

18. It's tricky (in some setups) to get enough distillate to measure—but do the best you can if you don't get much try to tweak the system for better results. Much can be learned from this lab even if the amounts of distillate are low.

Lab: Separating Ingredients

Data and Observations

Cranberry Juice

Observations of the liquid before heating: _____

_____

Observations of the remaining liquid in the sauce pan after heating: _____

_____

Observations of the distilled liquid in the collecting jar: _____

_____

Diet Cola

Observations of the liquid before heating: _____

_____

Observations of the remaining liquid in the sauce pan after heating: _____

_____

Observations of the distilled liquid in the collecting jar: _____

_____

Orange Soda

Observations of the liquid before heating: _____

_____

Observations of the remaining liquid in the sauce pan after heating: _____

_____

Observations of the distilled liquid in the collecting jar: _____

_____

Lab: Separating Ingredients

Data Table

Beverage	Amount of liquid in sauce pan before heating (mL)	Amount of liquid in sauce pan after heating (mL)	Amount of liquid in collection jar (mL)	Total amount of liquid after heating (mL)
Cranberry juice				
Diet cola				
Orange soda				

Analysis

1. In what section of the lab did you record quantitative data? In what section of the lab did you record qualitative data? _____

2. Using your observations, how can you conclude that a different liquid was collected in the collection jar than was poured into the sauce pan that was heated? _____
   _____

3. What liquid do you think was distilled into the collection vessel? Explain your answer. _____
   _____
   _____

4. What can you conclude about the relative boiling points between the liquid that was distilled and the substances that remained in the sauce pan after heating? _____
   _____
   _____

5. Add the amount of liquid in the sauce pan after heating with the amount of liquid in the collection jar. Write this number in the column representing the total amount of liquid after heating. Calculate the difference between the amounts of liquid you started with and the total amounts of liquid after heating. Are these values the same? Name at least three reasons why these values might not agree. _____
   _____
   _____
   _____

Conclusions

Keeping in mind that the goal of this lab was for you to separate liquid out of several common beverages through distillation, write an appropriate conclusion for your lab experiment.

Student Guide
Lesson 14: Acids and Bases

Lesson Objectives

- Compare properties of acids and bases.
- Determine whether a given solution is acidic, basic, or neutral.
- Recognize and label common acids and bases.
- Define pH and explain how it is determined.

PREPARE

Approximate lesson time is 60 minutes.

Materials

For the Student

- 🖳 Acids and Bases Review
- 🖳 Data Tables
- 🖳 The Colors, They Are A-Changin'
- baking soda
- blender
- measuring spoon - teaspoon
- strainer
- bowl, large
- cabbage, small red - about 1 lb
- cups, clear plastic (9)
- graduated cylinder
- jar, with lid - holds 1 L
- marker, permanent
- plastic spoons
- safety goggles
- vinegar, white
- water, distilled
- water, distilled - 500 mL

Keywords and Pronunciation

acid : a substance that is characterized by a sour taste and has a pH of less than 7

base : a substance that has a bitter taste and a slippery feel, and a pH of greater than 7

pH : a scale that measures the acidity or baseness of a solution

LEARN

Activity 1: Acids and Bases *(Online)*

Activity 2: Acids and Bases Review *(Online)*

Review what you have learned about acids and bases. Start by printing the Acids and Bases Review worksheet. When you're finished, place your completed lesson review worksheet in your Science Notebook.

Activity 3: The Colors, They Are A-Changin' *(Online)*

ASSESS

Lesson Assessment: Acids and Bases *(Offline)*

You will complete an offline assessment covering the main objectives of this lesson. Your learning coach will score this assessment.

Name _____ Date _____

Acids and Bases Review

Answers to Questions 1-3.

1. Classify each substance as an acid or base.

    a. HCl

    b. HNO_3

    c. NaOH

    d. LiOH

    e. NH_3

    f. H_2SO_4

2. What is the pH scale and what do the values represent?

3. Complete the table below.

Property	Acid	Base
pH		
taste		
ions released in water		
color of litmus paper		

Name _____   Date _____

The Colors, They Are A-Changin'

Introduction

Throughout this lesson you have explored properties of acids and bases. An acid yields an H^+ ion in water and a base yields an OH^- ion in water. A neutralization reaction is one in which an acid and a base are combined to form salt and water. In this lesson you will make cabbage juice to use as an indicator. Then you will test several household items to see if they are acids or bases.

Materials

Making the Indicator:

food blender
graduated cylinder
distilled water (500 mL)
small red cabbage (about 1 lb)
large bowl
wire strainer
jar with lid (holds at least 1 L)

Using the Indicator:

8-oz clear plastic drinking cups, 9
graduated cylinder
measuring spoons (teaspoon)
baking soda
white vinegar
distilled water
plastic spoons
permanent marker
safety goggles

Safety

If you choose to use more corrosive chemicals as listed in the Tips section, be sure to wear long sleeves, long pants, and protective gloves in addition to your safety goggles. If you spill any chemical on your skin, notify an adult immediately and flush the area with lots of cool water.

Procedures

Part I: Making the Indicator

1. Pour 500 mL of distilled water into the blender.

2. Tear or cut the red cabbage leaves into small pieces. Add the pieces to the blender containing the water.

3. Put the lid on the blender and blend the cabbage and water until the water does not seem to be getting any darker.

4. Pour the contents from the blender through the strainer and into the bowl.

5. You have now made an acid-base indicator. Pour it into a jar to keep it sterile (and because some people find the odor obnoxious!).

Part II: Testing for Acids and Bases

6. Using the marker, label the plastic cups 1 through 9.

7. Add 1 tsp (5 mL) of baking soda and 50 mL of distilled water to cup 1. Stir with a plastic spoon.

8. Add 1 tsp (5 mL) of baking soda and 50 mL of distilled water to cup 2. Stir with a plastic spoon.

9. Pour 50 mL of distilled water into each of cups 3 and 4.

10. Pour 50 mL of vinegar into each of cups 5 through 9. Rinse the cylinder before the next step.

11. Pour 20 mL of indicator juice into each of cups 1 through 6.

12. Observe the color of the solutions in each of the cups and record your observations in Data Table 1.

13. Pour the contents of cup 9 into cup 6. Observe the color change and record your observation in Data Table 2.

14. Pour the contents of cup 8 into cup 4. Observe the color change and record your observation in Data Table 2.

15. Pour the contents of cup 7 into cup 2. Be sure to do this in a sink or in a baking dish. Observe the color change and record your observation in Data Table 2.

Safety Tips

Any unused amount of indicator can be stored in the refrigerator. If you have time, you can also test other household chemicals to see a wider range of pH levels. Good substances to test include muriatic acid, lemon juice, lemon-lime soda, milk, ammonia, and drain cleaner. If you test these items, be sure to wear protective gloves, long sleeves, long pants and safety goggles, because some of these chemicals can be dangerous!

Data Tables

Expected Results

Data table

Cup	Solution Description	Solution Color
1	50 mL distilled water 1 tsp baking soda 20 mL indicator	
2	50 mL distilled water 1 tsp baking soda 20 mL indicator	
3	50 mL distilled water 20 mL indicator	
4	50 mL distilled water 20 mL indicator	
5	50 mL vinegar 20 mL indicator	
6	50 mL vinegar 20 mL indicator	

Data table 2

Cup #s	Mixture Description	Mixture Color
9 & 6	Cup 9 (50 mL vinegar) Cup 6 (vinegar and indicator)	
8 & 4	Cup 8 (50 mL vinegar) Cup 4 (water and indicator)	
7 & 2	Cup 7 (50 mL vinegar) Cup 2 (water, baking soda, indicator)	

Questions

1. What was the neutral solution you tested? What color is the indicator when it is in the presence of a neutral solution?

    _____

    _____

2. What was the acidic solution you tested? What color is the indicator when it is in the presence of an acid?

    _____

    _____

3. What was the basic solution you tested? What color is the indicator when it is in the presence of a base?

    _____

    _____

4. How is the pH of the combined solution (mixture cups 6 and 9) related to the pH of the initial solution in cup 6?

    _____

    _____

5. Refer to Data Table 2. How is the concentration of H$^+$ ions affected in cup 6 with the addition of the vinegar from cup 9?

_____

_____

_____

6. How is the pH of the combined solution (mixture of cups 8 and 4) related to the pH of the initial solution in cup 4?

_____

_____

7. Refer to Data Table 2. How is the concentration of H$^+$ ions affected in cup 4 with the addition of the vinegar from cup 8?

_____

_____

8. How is the pH of the combined solution (mixture of cups 2 and 7) related to the pH of the initial solution in cup 2?

_____

_____

9. Refer to Data Table 2. How is the concentration of H$^+$ ions affected in cup 2 with the addition of the vinegar from cup 7?

_____

_____

10. Which of the combinations that you performed in this activity demonstrated a neutralization reaction? How do you know, and what took place in this reaction?

_____

_____

_____

11. Write a summarizing sentence to explain the relationship between pH of solutions and the concentration of H$^+$ ions.

_____

_____

Name _____   Date _____

Acids and Bases Assessment

Answer Questions 1 – 4.

1. Explain how the pH of a solution is determined.

2. Create a table that compares the properties of acids and bases.

3. Explain how you can safely determine whether a given solution is acidic, basic, or neutral.

4. Draw a pH scale in the space below. Divide the scale into increments and label them from 0 to 14. Then label the scale to show where water, bleach, and vinegar would be located.

Student Guide
Lesson 16: Model Problems

Lesson Objectives

- Gain experience answering model problems related to topics of the previous lessons.

PREPARE

Approximate lesson time is 60 minutes.

LEARN
Activity 1: Chemistry *(Online)*

Student Guide
Lesson 17: Unit Review

Lesson Objectives

- Explain how chemical reactions occur.
- Interpret graphs showing the rates of chemical reactions.
- Compare the chemistry of ionic and covalent bonds.
- Explain what is modeled by a chemical formula.
- Balance chemical equations and explain what it means to balance such an equation.
- Compare the chemistry of acids and bases.

PREPARE

Approximate lesson time is 60 minutes.

LEARN
Activity 1: Chemistry *(Online)*

Student Guide
Lesson 18: Unit Assessment

Lesson Objectives

- Explain how chemical reactions occur.
- Explain what is modeled by a chemical formula.
- Compare the chemistry of acids and bases.
- Compare homogeneous mixtures (solutions) and heterogeneous mixtures.
- Interpret graphs showing the rates of chemical reactions.
- Compare the chemistry of ionic and covalent bonds.
- Balance chemical equations and explain what it means to balance such an equation.

PREPARE

Approximate lesson time is 60 minutes.

ASSESS

Unit Assessment: Chemistry, Part 1 (*Online*)

You will complete an online assessment of the main objectives covered so far in this unit. Follow the instructions online. Your assessment will be scored by the computer.

Unit Assessment: Chemistry, Part 2 (*Offline*)

Complete the offline part of the Unit Assessment. Your learning coach will score this part of the Assessment.

Student Guide
Lesson 1: Force

Have you ever experienced the thrill of an amusement park ride? A roller coaster can move you in a straight line very fast before taking you up and over a hill and through corkscrew turns. The forces acting on your body seem to pull you out of your seat, toss you from side to side, or make you feel heavier than you really are. Those forces and the motion that goes along with forces are the focus of this unit.

Lesson Objectives
- Define force as a push or a pull that can cause an object to move, stop moving, change speed, or change direction.
- Explain that a force has direction and strength (magnitude).
- Interpret a diagram to describe the forces acting on a specific object and their cumulative effect.
- Recognize that an object at rest, upon which balanced forces are acting, will not change its state of motion.
- Identify a variety of forces such as gravity, magnetism, friction, spring, and electrical.

PREPARE

Approximate lesson time is 60 minutes.

Materials
For the Student
- 🖥 Force Review
- 🖥 Crashmallow!
  thread
  marshmallows, mini
  paper - 8 1/2 x 11
  pencil
  ruler, metric
  table
  tape, masking
  toy, car

Keywords and Pronunciation
force : a push or pull that can cause an object to move, stop moving, change speed, or change direction

friction : a force that resists motion between two objects that are in contact

gravity : a universal force that every mass exerts on every other mass

newton : an SI unit of force represented by the letter N

LEARN
Activity 1: Force *(Online)*

Activity 2: Force *(Online)*

Review what you have learned about force. Start by printing the Force Review worksheet. When you are finished, place your completed worksheet in your Science Notebook.

Activity 3: Crashmallow! *(Online)*

Activity

The concept of force has many applications in your daily life. You probably ride in a car on a regular basis. Print Crashmallow! to learn about the effects of force on a car passenger.

ASSESS
Lesson Assessment: Force (*Online*)

You will complete an online assessment covering the main objectives of this lesson. Your assessment will be scored by the computer.

Name _____ Date _____

Force Review

Use the words from this list to fill in the blanks in sentences 1-3 below. The words may be used more than once.

  direction
  stop
  pull
  magnitude
  balanced
  speed
  push
  move

1. A force is a _____ or a _____. It can cause an object at rest to_____. It can cause an object that is moving to change _____ or _____ or to _____ moving.

2. A force has both _____ and _____.

3. An object with _____ forces will not change position.

4. Draw a force diagram for a jet airliner (use a solid circle to represent the airliner) cruising at a constant altitude and constant speed. When forces are equal, the length of the arrows should be equal. If one force is twice as large as another force, the arrow showing the larger force should be drawn twice as long. Hint: There are four forces acting on the jet.

Name _____   Date _____

Crashmallow!

Materials:

mini marshmallow
toy car (or anything with wheels)
masking tape
pencil
piece of paper (8 ½ x 11 in.)
ruler
tabletop (large enough to tape the paper and pencil to with room to spare)
piece of thread (15 cm long)

Procedures:

1. Tape the paper to the left of center on the tabletop. The longest side of the paper should be parallel to the edge of the table.

2. Tape the pencil along the right edge of the paper.

3. Position the car to the right of the paper approximately 30 cm from the pencil. The paper should be on the opposite side of the pencil. The car should be perpendicular to the pencil.

4. Place the marshmallow on the hood of the car. Do not attach it to the car but just allow the marshmallow to rest there.

5. Push the car (and let it go) so it rolls toward the pencil. Be sure to push hard enough so the car will hit the pencil.

6. Watch what happens to the marshmallow. On the paper, mark the location where the marshmallow landed and label it trial 1 to indicate that this is the first trial.

7. Repeat the experiment for a second trial, pushing the car even harder than you did the first time.

8. Watch what happens to the marshmallow. On the paper, mark the location where the marshmallow landed and label this point as trial 2 to indicate the second trial.

9. Repeat the experiment for a third trial, pushing the car even harder than the first two trials. Observe what happens and mark the location where the marshmallow landed, being sure to label it trial 3.

10. Use the thread to tie the marshmallow to the car. Be sure the thread does not interfere with the wheels of the car. This will be the setup you will you use for your fourth trial.

11. Position the car approximately 30 cm from the pencil, as you did in the first three trials.

12. Push the car so it rolls toward the pencil and then hits it. Observe what happens to the marshmallow.

Questions:

1. What happened to the marshmallow the first time the car hit the pencil? The second? The third?

_____

_____

_____

2. Explain how the concept of force relates to what you observed for the car and the marshmallow in the first three trials of the experiment.

_____

_____

_____

3. Explain what happened to the marshmallow in the fourth trial and why it happened that way.

_____

_____

_____

4. Think of yourself as the marshmallow, but inside a real car. What would happen to you if the car stopped suddenly in an accident? How would the results differ if you weren't wearing your seat belt?

_____

_____

_____

Student Guide
Lesson 2: Gravitational Force

If you throw a ball into the air, will it travel upward forever? Of course not! It will fall back down to earth. And, if you drop a book, feather, or bowling ball, they won't float, they will all fall to the ground. The force of gravity here on earth makes this happen.

Lesson Objectives

- Define gravity as a universal force that every mass exerts on every other mass.
- Explain that the weight of objects varies at different locations in the universe, due to differences in gravitational force; the mass of objects remains constant.
- Apply Newton's Law of Universal Gravitation to explain how gravity acts upon all objects in the universe.
- Describe fundamental notions of how scientists think gravity shaped planets, stars, and solar systems.

PREPARE

Approximate lesson time is 60 minutes.

Materials

For the Student

    📖 Gravity in Action

       paper - 8 1/2 x 11

       tape measure

       tennis ball

Keywords and Pronunciation

force : a push or pull that can cause an object to move, stop moving, change speed, or change direction

gravity : a universal force that every mass exerts on every other mass

law of universal gravitation : the concept that gravitation occurs everywhere in the universe

mass : The quantity of matter in an object.

mass : the amount of matter in an object

weight : a measure of the gravitational force exerted on an object

---

LEARN
Activity 1: Gravitational Force (Online)

Activity 2: Gravitational Force *(Online)*

Instructions

Write your answers for Questions 1–5 on the lines.

1. How do the masses of two objects affect the gravitational force between them?

_____

_____

2. How does the distance between two objects affect the gravitational force between them?

_____

_____

3. If a person travels from earth to the moon, what changes—his mass or her weight?

_____

4. In a space trip outside the solar system, astronauts will float inside their spacecraft unless they are strapped down. When you ride in a car or bus, you do not float up out of your seat. Explain why these two situations are different.

_____

_____

_____

5. Venus and Earth have about the same mass. Would you expect the gravitational force between Venus and the sun to be stronger or weaker than the gravitational force between earth and the sun? Explain your answer.

_____

_____

Activity 3: Gravity in Action *(Online)*

ASSESS

Lesson Assessment: Gravitational Force, Part 1 *(Online)*

You will complete an online assessment covering the main objectives of this lesson. Your assessment will be scored by the computer.

Lesson Assessment: Gravitational Force, Part 2 *(Offline)*

You will complete an offline assessment covering the main objectives of this lesson. Your learning coach will score this assessment.

Name _____ Date _____

Gravity In Action

Materials

tennis ball
1 sheet 8 ½" x 11" notebook paper
tape measure

Procedures

1. Hold the tennis ball and the paper (horizontally) the same distance from the ground. You may wish to have someone else help you measure the distance from each of your hands to the ground to make sure the distances are equal. Make a prediction about which object will hit the ground first when you let go of them.

2. Drop both objects at the same time. Observe which object hits the ground first.

3. Repeat Steps 1 and 2 at least two more times to make sure your results are accurate.

4. Now, crumple up the paper into a ball shape that is about the same diameter as the tennis ball.

5. Repeat Steps 1 through 3 with the tennis ball and the crumpled paper. Before you drop the objects, make a prediction about which object will hit the ground first.

6. Compress the paper into the smallest possible ball you can make. Repeat Steps 1 through 3 again with the tennis ball and the tightly-crumpled paper.

Questions

1. Why do you think the tennis ball hit the ground more quickly than the flat sheet of paper?

_____

_____

2. What happened when you repeated the activity with the crumpled sheet of paper and the tennis ball?

_____

_____

3. What do you think would happen if you dropped a bowling ball and a tennis ball from the same height? Why?

_____

_____

4. What does this activity tell you about the effects of gravity on all objects in the universe?

_____

_____

Name _____   Date _____

Gravitational Force Lesson Assessment

Think about movies you have seen that show an astronaut walking on the surface of the moon, then complete Question 1.

1. On the moon, astronauts bounce slowly as they try to move across the moon's surface. Why does this happen?

_____

_____

_____

_____

© 2013 K12 Inc. All rights reserved.
Copying or distributing without K12's written consent is prohibited.

Student Guide
Lesson 3: Motion

Motion is a part of your everyday life. From the time you get up in the morning until you go to bed at night, motion comes into play. Sometimes you cause motion, like when you walk, run, or throw a baseball. Sometimes another object, such as a car, bus, or airplane, moves you. You know what it feels like to move quickly or stop suddenly. Let's see how science measures and describes the relationships between motion, speed, and distance.

Lesson Objectives

- Define motion as a change in position within a certain amount of time.
- Explain that motion is established with respect to a frame of reference.
- Explain that the motion of an object can be described according to its position, direction, and speed.
- Interpret diagrams that represent motion.

PREPARE

Approximate lesson time is 60 minutes.

Materials

> For the Student
>> 🖥 Motion Review

Keywords and Pronunciation

coordinate system : a set of reference points, lines, and/or directions by which the position of any point can be described

displacement : the distance and the direction from a reference point of an object that has undergone motion

reference point : a point from which the position of other objects can be described

rotational motion : when objects spin in place

translational motion : type of motion in an object that results in a change of position from point A to point B

vibrational motion : rapid back and forth movement of the kind found in particles that make up a substance

---

LEARN
Activity 1: Motion *(Online)*

Activity 2: Motion *(Online)*

ASSESS
Lesson Assessment: Motion (*Online*)

You will complete an online assessment covering the main objectives of this lesson. Your assessment will be scored by the computer.

LEARN
Activity 3: Activity (*Online*)

Name _____   Date _____

Motion Review

Fill in the blank for Questions 1-5. Use the following word list. Do not use any of the words more than once. You may not need to use all of the words.

distance

coordinate systems

translational

rotational

molecular

displacement

time

reference point

relative

1. To describe the position of an object accurately, scientists use _____ .

2. In science, we have to describe the motion of an object _____ to other objects.

3. The motion of an object involves changes in both distance and _____ .

4. An object moves along a straight line. It moves +3.0 cm and then −5.0 cm. It has a

    _____ of −2.0 cm and travels a _____ of 8.0 cm.

5. Motion from one place to another is called _____ motion.

In the space below, draw a picture to help you answer Question 6.

6. An object moves 3.0 km east, 4.0 km south, 6.0 km north, and 3.0 km west. What distance has the object traveled? What is the object's displacement?

Name _____   Date _____

Use the graph below to answer Questions 7-9.

Displacement vs. Time for Two Runners

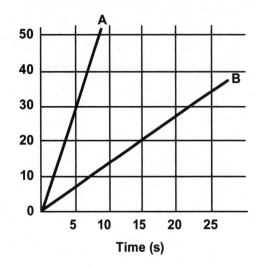

7.   Which runner ran the fastest?_____

8.   Which runner had the greater displacement?_____

9.   Which runner moved 20 m in 15 s? _____

Student Guide
Lesson 4: Lab: Calculating Speed

Lesson Objectives

- Design an experiment to test a hypothesis or to gather information; state the purpose of the experiment.

PREPARE

Approximate lesson time is 60 minutes.

Materials

For the Student

🖥 Calculating Speed

LEARN
Activity 1: Calculating Speed *(Online)*

ASSESS

Lesson Assessment: LAB: Calculating Speed (*Online*)

Have an adult review your answers to the LAB: Calculating Speed, and input the results online.

Name _____ Date _____

Calculating Speed

Goals

- Calculate a quantity that is derived from other, more basic, quantities that are measured.

- Draw conclusions based on data gathered in an experiment.

Materials

- virtual cart and track

- virtual centimeter ruler

- virtual meter stick

- virtual stopwatch

Open the Virtual Lab: Speed Lab.

Procedure for Exercise A: Set-up and Measurement

The purpose of this exercise is to familiarize yourself with the virtual spring-driven cart and the components that make it work.

1. Drag a gear into place in the mechanism, wind, and release the spring. What did you observe?

2. Measure the diameter in centimeters of each gear using the ruler. Enter each value on the gear itself.

3. Use the meter stick to measure and mark a finish line 1 meter from the starting position of the cart.

Procedures for Exercise B: Form Hypothesis

The purpose of this exercise is to make a hypothesis about the effect of changing an independent variable.

1. Think about what you obsereved when you released the spring after winding the car. Based on what you saw, think about what effect you would expect different diameter gears to have on the speed of the car.

2. Use the dropdown to select your hypothesis, and copy your choice here.

    I think with larger gears the car moves _____ .

Procedures for Exercise C: Make Observations

The purpose of this exercise is to record data on the performance of your cart based on its configuration.

1. Your cart begins this activity with whichever gear was in the cart at the end of the Set-up Exercise. Wind the spring and click the catch to release the cart.

2. Click Stop on the timer as the cart crosses the Finish line. The timer shows the amount of time needed for the cart to travel 1 meter.

3. Look at the Data Table. Find where it shows the diameter of the gear that's in the cart, and enter the time (in seconds) in the first blank box beneath the gear you're testing. Click Reset on the timer and return the cart to the left side of the track.

4. Try two (2) more trials using the same gear diameter. For each trial record the time in the blank box below where you entered the previous trial's data.

5. Remove the gear and replace it with another. Repeat steps 1 – 4.

6. In order to finish gathering data, you need at least 3 trials with each diameter gear. When you have all the data you need, you will return to the progress screen. Click Hypothesis to state your hypothesis and test it using the data you have gathered.

Data Table

Gear diameter (cm)	Trial	Time (s)
	Trial 1	
	Trial 2	
	Trial 3	
	Trial 1	
	Trial 2	
	Trial 3	
	Trial 1	
	Trial 2	
	Trial 3	

Procedures for Exercise D: Analyze Data

The purpose of this exercise is to analyze the data gathered about the performance and use it to test your hypothesis about the effect of gears on cart speed.

1. On the graph provided, label the horizontal axis with the independent variable (gear size) and the vertical axis with the dependent variable (velocity).

2. Plot each data point on the graph. You should have 9 data points all together, in 3 groups of 3 points each. In each group, if there is any difference in the points, it should only be a small difference in velocity. Any points that are very far from the others in the group may be bad data.

3. Calculate the average time it took for the car to travel 1 meter when equipped with each of the gears. Recall that to find the average you will add the values for each trial and divide by the number of trials. Record these average times in the Speed Data Table.

4. Next, calculate the speed at which the car traveled for each movement type. Do this by dividing the distance traveled (in meters) by the time it took (in seconds). In equation form: speed = distance / time.

5. Record your speed in the Speed Data Table.

6. For each gear, plot a point on the Gear Diameter vs. Speed graph.

Speed Data Table

Gear diameter (cm)	Distance Traveled (m)	Average Time (s)	Speed (m/s)

Analysis

1. What tool(s) did you use to measure in this activity? What units were used?

2. What units for speed did you use in this activity?

3. Did you use a tool to measure speed? If yes, what tool did you use? If no, how did you determine speed?

4. Can you think of a situation in which an instrument measures and indicates speed?

Conclusion

Write a brief summary for each of the following questions.

1. What was the purpose of this experiment?

2. How did you determine speed? Include your measurements and calculations.

3. Look at the results of your data in the graph. Which gear caused the car to go fastest? Which version of the car was slowest?

4. Does the answer to the previous question support or refute your hypothesis?

Student Guide
Lesson 5: Speed and Velocity

Lesson Objectives

- Define speed as the distance an object has traveled divided by time.
- Solve problems about speed.
- Define velocity as the speed of an object in a certain direction.
- Interpret information about speed and velocity presented in tables and graphs.

PREPARE

Approximate lesson time is 60 minutes.

Materials

For the Student

    📖 Speed and Velocity Review

    📖 Vacation Time

      atlas - continental United States, or Internet website with distance information

Keywords and Pronunciation

speed : rate of motion, measured as distance divided by the time required to travel that distance

velocity (veh-LAH-suh-tee) : speed in a specific direction

LEARN
Activity 1: Speed and Velocity *(Online)*

Activity 2: Speed and Velocity *(Online)*

Review what you have learned about speed and velocity. When finished, place your completed lesson review sheet in your Science Notebook.

Activity 3: Vacation Time *(Online)*

ASSESS

Lesson Assessment: Speed and Velocity (*Online*)

: You will complete an online assessment covering the main objectives of this lesson. Your assessment will be scored by the computer.

Name _____   Date _____

Speed and Velocity Review

Use the words from this list to fill in the blanks in 1-5 below. The words may be used more than once and may be used as either singular or plural.

speed

velocity

time

table

distance

graph

direction

1. Average speed is the_____an object travels divided by the_____ it takes.

2. The velocity of an object is its_____in a certain_____.

3. The steepness of the line on a position-time graph measures the object's_____.

4. Displacement always includes a_____ and is used in measuring

    _____ .

5. Average speed and velocity may be calculated from position/time data found in a

    _____or a_____ .

Use the following table to answer Questions 6 and 7.

The Flight of a Jet

Position (km)	Time (s)
0	0
+1	10
+5	30
+10	50
+4	70
+4	90

Name _____   Date _____

6. What was the average velocity of the jet from +5.0 km to +10 km? Show your work.

_____

_____

_____

_____

_____

7. What was the velocity of the jet from 70 s to 90 s? Explain your answer.

_____

_____

_____

_____

_____

Name _____   Date _____

Vacation Time

Introduction

Have you ever taken a long car trip with your family? Sometimes it can be difficult to predict how long the trip will take. Road construction, traffic, and other factors can affect the speed at which the car can travel. Most technologies that people use (the Internet, GPS systems, etc.) calculate driving times based on an average speed. They take into account the number of miles that must be driven, and the posted speeds on the roads they recommend. To determine average speed, we use the formula: $v = s/t$.

For example, if the driving distance from Chicago, IL, to Atlanta, GA, is 710 miles, and we drive that distance in 14 hours, we would use the formula in this way:
$v = 710$ miles / 14 hours = 50.71 mph
Our average speed would be 50.71 miles per hour.

Materials

Student needs access to either an Internet website that provides distance information between cities in the continental United States, or a road atlas of the continental United States.

Procedures

1. Look at each driving trip listed in the Data Chart below.

2. Use the Internet to find the driving directions from the first location to the second location. Write the total number of miles for each trip on the Data Chart. Round the information to the nearest mile.

3. Using the number of hours listed on the Data Chart calculate the average speed for each trip. Fill in the information on the chart. Round the average speed to the nearest hundredth.

Data Chart

Trip	Miles	Driving Time	Average Speed
Los Angeles, CA, to Topeka, KS		23 hours	
Portland, OR, to Cincinnati, OH		35 hours	
Albany, NY, to Jacksonville, FL		20 hours	
Austin, TX, to Washington, DC		22 hours	
Reno, NV, to Tulsa, OK		26 hours	

Questions

1. What would happen to the average speed of the trip from Reno to Tulsa if you increased the driving time to 30 hours?

    _____

    _____

2. What would happen to the average speed of the trip from Portland to Cincinnati if you decreased the driving time to 30 hours?

    _____

    _____

3. What formula is used to determine average speed?

    _____

Student Guide
Lesson 6: Measuring Speed and Velocity

Lesson Objectives

- Explain that velocity in one dimension may be positive or negative while speed always has a positive value.
- Solve problems about speed and velocity using graphs, drawings, and computation.

PREPARE

Approximate lesson time is 60 minutes.

Materials

For the Student

- 💻 Graph Paper
- 💻 Keep On Rolling!

LEARN
Activity 1: Measuring Speed and Velocity *(Online)*

Activity 2: Measuring Speed and Velocity *(Online)*

Activity 3: Keep On Rolling! *(Online)*

ASSESS

Lesson Assessment: Measuring Speed and Velocity, Part 1 (*Online*)

You will complete an online assessment covering the main objectives of this lesson. Your assessment will be scored by the computer.

Lesson Assessment: Measuring Speed and Velocity, Part 2 (*Offline*)

You will complete an offline assessment covering the main objectives of this lesson. Your learning coach will score this assessment.

Name _____   Date _____

Name   Date

Keep On Rolling!

Imagine that you are a skateboarder poised and ready to push yourself onto a run at the skate park.
You can predict what will happen to your velocity during each part of the run and graph your results.

Materials

pencil

graph paper

Procedure

1.   Study the run that the skateboarder in the illustration is about to take. Think about the changes
     in velocity that will occur with each change in direction.

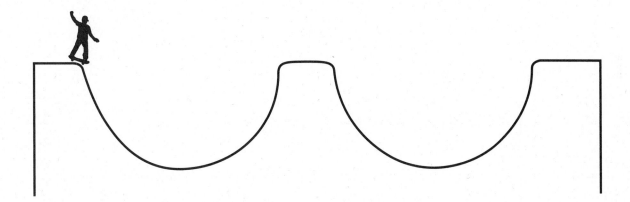

2.   On graph paper, create a simple graph like the one shown below.

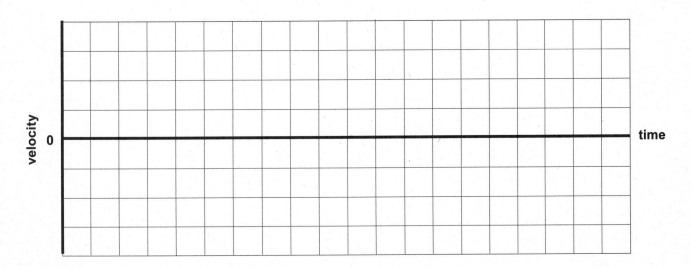

Name _____   Date _____

3. For this question you will need to use the graph you created in Procedure 2. Use what you know about velocity to graph the velocity of the skateboarder at the skate park. You do not need to calculate specific numeric values, just draw lines on the graph to show when velocity increases or decreases and by approximately how much it increases or decreases.

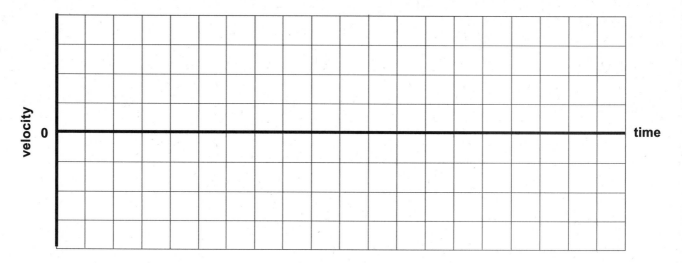

4. Write an explanation for why you created your graph the way you did.

Name _____   Date _____

Measuring Speed and Velocity Lesson Assessment

1. Explain why average velocity in one dimension can be positive or negative.

   _____

   _____

2. Can speed ever be negative? Explain.

   _____

   _____

Student Guide
Lesson 8: Acceleration

Lesson Objectives

- Define acceleration as the rate of change of velocity.
- Explain that changes in velocity may be caused by changes in speed and direction.
- For motion in one dimension, distinguish among positive, negative, and no acceleration.

PREPARE

Approximate lesson time is 60 minutes.

Materials

For the Student

- ▣ Lesson Review
- ▣ Acceleration

books, thick - or blocks

marble - 1 glass

stopwatch

ruler, metric

table - at least 1.5 m long

tape, masking

Keywords and Pronunciation

acceleration : a change in velocity over time

deceleration : Deceleration is a way to say that an object is slowing down. It should not be confused with negative acceleration (since negative acceleration could be speeding up in a negative direction OR slowing down in a positive direction).

LEARN
Activity 1: Acceleration *(Online)*

Activity 2: Acceleration *(Online)*

Review what you have learned about acceleration. When finished, place your completed lesson review sheet in your Science Notebook.

Activity 3: Acceleration *(Online)*

ASSESS

Lesson Assessment: Acceleration, Part 1 (*Online*)

You will complete an online assessment covering the main objectives of this lesson. Your assessment will be scored by the computer.

Lesson Assessment: Acceleration, Part 2 (*Offline*)

You will complete an offline assessment covering the main objectives of this lesson. Your learning coach will score this assessment.

Name _____   Date _____

Acceleration Review

Identify each of the following as having either positive acceleration (+a), negative acceleration (-a), or not acceleration (na).

1.   A car moving away from a stop sign   _____

2.   A car coming to a stop _____

3.   A car moving at constant speed on a straight road _____

Short Answer

4.   What can be changing if an object is accelerating?

   _____

5.   Explain why an object accelerates when it comes to a stop.

   _____

   _____

6.   Planets are constantly accelerating as they orbit the sun, even when they are not changing speed. Explain.

   _____

Fill in the blank for Questions 6-8. Use the following word list. You may not use all of the words on the list. Do not use any of the words more than once.

speed
zero
positive
velocity
acceleration
negative
direction

7.   In order for an object to be accelerating, its _____ must be changing.

© 2013 K12 Inc. All rights reserved.
Copying or distributing without K12's written consent is prohibited.

8. An object that moves at a constant speed in a constant direction has _____ acceleration.

9. A graph of velocity vs. time depicts _____ .

Name _____   Date _____

Acceleration

Materials

table (at least 1.5m long)
books or blocks
masking tape
1 glass marble
centimeter ruler or tape measure
stopwatch

Procedures

1. Elevate one end of the table by placing books or sturdy blocks under the legs. It should be elevated about 20°.

2. Place a 10 cm length of masking tape at least 20 cm from one end and parallel to the end of the table. Place two more 10 cm pieces of tape on the table so that each piece is 50 cm from the next.

3. Release the marble from the piece of tape nearest the high end of the table and use the stopwatch to time how long it takes the marble to roll to the first 50 cm marker. Record this value in the Data Table.

4. Repeat Step 3 four more times and calculate an average value for the time.

5. Next, release the marble from rest at the same tape marker at the high end of the table and time how long it takes to roll from the second piece of tape to the third. Record this value in the Data Table. Run a total of five trials and calculate the average time.

6. Use your data of distances and average times to determine the average velocity for the first 50 cm and the second 50 cm intervals. Calculate the average velocity for the entire trip by using the total distance (100 cm) and the sum of the average time values for the 50 cm intervals. Be sure to include the appropriate units in your calculation.

7. Assuming the starting velocity to be 0 cm/s, calculate the average acceleration for the first 50 cm and for the second 50 cm intervals. Calculate the average acceleration of the entire trip by using the average velocity for the total trip as determined in the previous step and the total average time. Be sure to include the appropriate units in your calculations.

Data Table

Interval	Trial	Time (seconds)
First 50 cm interval	Trial 1	
	Trial 2	
	Trial 3	
	Trial 4	
	Trial 5	
	Average time	
Second 50 cm interval	Trial 1	
	Trial 2	
	Trial 3	
	Trial 4	
	Trial 5	
	Average time	

Questions

1. What was the average velocity for the first 50 cm, the second 50 cm, and for the entire trip of 100 cm? Be sure to include the appropriate units with your values.

   _____

   _____

   _____

   _____

   _____

2. What was the average acceleration for the first 50 cm, the second 50 cm, and for the entire trip of 100 cm? Be sure to include the appropriate units with your values.

   _____

   _____

   _____

   _____

   _____

   _____

3. Acceleration implies a force. What force is acting on the objects?

   _____

4. Do you think your data and calculated values would have been different if the table angle had been higher or lower? Explain your answer.

   _____

   _____

   _____

5. Would the marble accelerate if the table were completely level? How about if the table was removed and the marble was simply dropped vertically, rather than rolled down the table?

   _____

   _____

Name _____   Date _____

Acceleration Assessment

Use the graph to answer Questions 1–4.

The following graph describes the motion of a football player returning a kick off.

Velocity vs. Time for a Player Returning a Kick Off

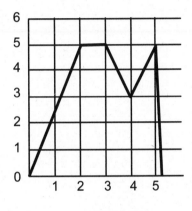

Velocity
(m/s east)

Time (s)

1. What was the player's acceleration from 0 to 2 s? _____

2. What was the player's acceleration from 2 s to 3 s?_____

3. Is the player's acceleration positive or negative between 3 and 4 s? _____

4. At what time did the player get tackled?_____

Student Guide
Lesson 9: Newton's First Law of Motion

Lesson Objectives

- Explain Newton's First Law of Motion.
- Recognize that when forces remain balanced, the velocity of an object will remain constant, and when the forces are unbalanced, the velocity of an object will change.
- Describe situations that demonstrate Newton's First Law of Motion.

PREPARE

Approximate lesson time is 60 minutes.

Materials

For the Student

    📖 Lesson Review

    📖 Acting Forces

      marbles - bag

      chalk

      flat surface - outside or on hard, flat tile

Keywords and Pronunciation

friction : a force that resists motion between two objects that are in contact

inertia (ih-NUHR-shuh) : the quality of an object that resists a change in motion or resists a change in the resting state

---

LEARN
Activity 1: Newton's First Law of Motion *(Online)*

Activity 2: Newton's First Law of Motion *(Online)*

Activity 3: Acting Forces *(Online)*

ASSESS

Lesson Assessment: Newton's First Law of Motion (*Online*)

You will complete an online assessment covering the main objectives of this lesson. Your assessment will be scored by the computer.

Name _____   Date _____

Newton's First Law of Motion Lesson Review

Use the words from this list to fill in the blanks in the paragraph below. The words may be used more than once and may be used as either singular or plural.

velocity

friction

unbalanced

rest

mass

inertia

1. Newton's First Law of Motion deals with objects at _____ and objects in constant motion.

2. Newton said that objects will not change their state of motion unless an_____ force acts on them.

3. _____is a measure of an object's _____.

4. When the forces that act on an object are balanced, the_____of the object remains constant.

5. When a bus starts moving, you feel pushed back because of _____ .

6. An object in motion can be slowed down by _____ .

7. Complete the following table about an airplane in flight.

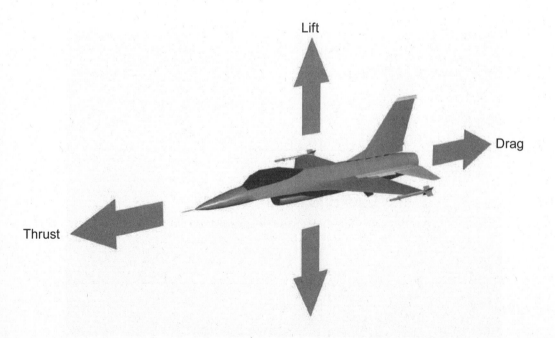

Lift (N)	Weight (N)	Thrust (N)	Drag (N)	Motion
6,000	6,000	12,000	11,500	
5,000	6,000	12,000	12,000	
6,000		12,000		Velocity will stay constant.
7,000	6,000	13,000	12,000	

Name _____ Date _____

Acting Forces

Materials

bag of marbles

chalk

flat surface such as an outdoor sidewalk or a flat tile surface

In the 1930s, a marble game called Ringer became very popular among American children. All you needed to play the game was a bag of marbles and something to draw a large circle with on the sidewalk. Children would collect marbles, and even have a lucky marble that they would use as their shooter. In this activity, you will see how Newton's First Law of Motion affects the outcome of Ringer.

Procedure

1. Using chalk, draw a large circle on the sidewalk. The diameter of the circle should be as close to 10 feet as possible.

2. Place all of the marbles but one in a + pattern in the center of the circle. The remaining marble will be your shooter.

3. Kneel outside the circle. Make a loose fist with your thumb out. Place your hand near the ground, but not touching, with your knuckles facing down. Place the marble on your thumb.

4. Use your thumb to shoot the marble towards the marbles in the center of the circle. (This motion is similar to that used when flipping a coin.) This may take some practice.

5. When you hit the marbles in the center, observe what happens to the marbles you hit. Observe what happens to the marble you used as the shooter.

6. In Ringer, the object is to shoot marbles out of the ring, while keeping the shooter marble inside the ring.

7. Continue to play the game until you have shot all of the marbles out of the ring.

Questions

1. What affect did the force of your thumb have on the shooter marble?

_____

_____

Name _____ Date _____

2. When the shooter marble hit another marble, what happened to that other marble? Which marble acted as a force?

_____
_____
_____
_____
_____

3. What happened to the shooter marble when it hit another marble?

_____
_____

Student Guide
Lesson 10: Mass and Weight

Lesson Objectives
- Describe an object's mass as the quantity of matter it contains (measured in kg or g).
- Describe the weight of an object as the magnitude of the earth's gravitational force acting upon it.
- Explain that the greater the mass of an object, the more force is needed to change its velocity.

PREPARE

Approximate lesson time is 60 minutes.

Materials
For the Student
- 🖳 Lesson Review
- 🖳 Heave, Ho!
  scale, spring
  bottle, plastic 500 ml
  index card
  metal rod
  string

Keywords and Pronunciation
mass : the amount of matter in an object
weight : a measure of the gravitational force exerted on an object

LEARN
Activity 1: Mass and Weight *(Online)*

Activity 2: Mass and Weight *(Online)*

Activity 3: Heave, Ho! *(Online)*

ASSESS

Lesson Assessment: Mass and Weight (*Online*)
You will complete an online assessment covering the main objectives of this lesson. Your assessment will be scored by the computer.

Name _____   Date _____

Lesson Review

Use the words from this list to fill in the blanks in the paragraphs below. The words may be used more than once and may be used as either singular or plural.

weight
mass
formula
scale
newton
balance
g or kg
acceleration due to gravity

The _____ of an object does not change if you move it to another location in our solar system. However, its _____ depends on where in the universe it is measured. Mass is measured with a _____ and weight is measured with a _____ . _____ is a force, but _____ is not. The units of mass are _____ while the units of weight are _____ .

You can calculate the _____ of an object if you know its_____ and a value for_____ . It is harder to change the velocity of an object with greater _____ than to change the velocity of one with smaller _____ . Mass and_____ are not the same thing. When dealing with _____ , you must be careful to use the correct value.

Name _____ Date _____

Heave, Ho!

Materials

spring scale
bottle, plastic 500ml
metal rod
index card
string
Science Notebook

You have read about the differences between mass and weight. Mass is the quantity of matter an object contains. Weight is the magnitude of the earth's gravitational force acting upon an object. If you went to the Moon, your weight would be much less than it is on Earth, but your mass would stay the same. It is the mass of an object that determines the amount of force necessary to change the velocity of that object.

Procedures

1. Fill the bottle with water. Use the spring scale to measure the weight of the bottle, metal rod, and index card. To measure the index card and the metal rod, you will need to tie a piece of string to each one and tie them to the spring scale. You can use a pencil to poke a hole in the index card for the string. Record the measurements in your Science Notebook. Keep the strings tied to the metal rod and the index card.

2. Hook the bottle to the spring scale. Place the bottle on its side on a flat surface. Use the spring scale to drag the bottle across the surface. Look at the measurement shown on the spring scale as you drag. This is the amount of force needed to move the bottle. Record the measurement in your Science Notebook.

3. Now lay the metal rod on the ground. Using the spring scale tied to the string on the metal rod, drag the metal rod across the flat surface. Look at the measurement shown on the spring scale and record it in your Science Notebook. Repeat with the index card.

Questions

1. Which item took the most force to drag? Which item took the least amount of force to drag?

   _____

   _____

2. What effect does mass have on velocity?

   _____

   _____

3. What differences would you have in your results in an area that has zero gravity?

   _____

   _____

Student Guide
Lesson 11: Newton's Second Law of Motion

Lesson Objectives

- Explain Newton's Second Law of Motion.
- Define acceleration as a change in velocity per unit of time.
- Explain that the acceleration of an object depends on its mass and the total amount of force applied to it.
- Solve problems using the formula F = ma.

PREPARE

Approximate lesson time is 60 minutes.

Materials

For the Student

 🖳 Lesson Review

 🖳 Going Places

  colored pencils - 2 colors

  washers - 3 metal

  cardboard - sheet that is at least 3 cm bigger than protractor on all sides

  protractor - plastic

  scissors

  string

LEARN
Activity 1: Newton's Second Law of Motion (Online)

Activity 2: Newton's Second Law of Motion (Online)

Activity 3: Going Places (Online)

ASSESS

Lesson Assessment: Newton's Second Law of Motion (Online)

You will complete an online assessment covering the main objectives of this lesson. Your assessment will be scored by the computer.

Name _____   Date _____

Newton's Second Law of Motion
Lesson Review

Use the words from this list to fill in the blanks in questions 1-3 below. The words may be used more than once and may be used as either singular or plural.

double

unbalanced

mass

time

acceleration

m/s²

velocity

accelerate

force

Newton's second law of motion says the acceleration of an object depends on the _____ of the object and the _____ acting on the object. If you _____ the push or pull on an object, the acceleration will double. The units of acceleration are _____ and acceleration is defined as a change in _____ per unit of _____.

The equation *F=ma* represents Newton's second law of motion. The *F* stands for a(n) _____ force. This type of force is needed to make a mass _____ The equation may be rearranged to solve for _____ or _____.

1. How much force is needed to accelerate a 0.50-kg ball at 50 m/s²?

2. What is the acceleration of a bicycle if the bicycle plus the rider have a mass of 75 kg and the net force on the bicycle is 375 N?

Name _____   Date _____

3.   What is the mass of a toy rocket if a force of 65 N produces an acceleration of 250m/s²?

Name _____ Date _____

Going Places

Materials

plastic protractor

cardboard that is at least 3 cm bigger (on all sides) than the protractor

2 colored pencils

scissors

string

3 metal washers

Science Notebook

Procedures

Part 1: Building an Accelerometer

1. Place the protractor on the cardboard and trace around its edges with one of the pencils.

2. If there is a hole at the crosshairs on the protractor's flat edge, in the center, trace the hole onto the cardboard. If there is no hole, make a mark on the cardboard so the mark aligns with the center of the protractor's flat edge.

3. Mark every 5 degrees on the cardboard using the protractor and the first colored pencil.

4. Remove the protractor from the cardboard.

5. The side of the cardboard with the tracing on it will be the front of the cardboard.

6. Now use the other colored pencil and add the Acceleration Scale information from the third column of the Data Table to the tracing of the protractor. The angles in the table will not fall exactly on the marks you made on the cardboard. It is okay to estimate to the nearest degree between the 5-degree marks that you made. Also note that each amount of acceleration will occur at two different angles on the protractor.

7. Tie the three washers to one end of the string.

8. Using a sharp pencil, punch out the tracing of the protractor's hole or the mark indicating the center of the flat edge of the protractor (if there was no hole).

9. Put the end of the string with no washers through this punched hole. When hanging vertically, the washers should be approximately 2 cm below the radius of the traced protractor but above the bottom of the cardboard.

10. Tie a knot in the string on the reverse side of the protractor so the string will not be pulled through the hole.

11. You have just constructed an accelerometer!

Name _____   Date _____

Data Table for Homemade Horizontal Accelerometer

Angle (degrees)	Angle (degrees)	Acceleration Scale (m/s²)
90	90	0
85	95	1
79	101	2
74	106	3
68	112	4
65	116	5
59	121	6
55	125	7
51	129	8
49	131	9
45	135	10
41	139	12
34	146	15
27	153	20
22	158	25
18	162	30
14	166	40
10	170	50
4	176	100

Name _____ Date _____

Procedures

Part 2: Using the Accelerometer

1. To use the accelerometer, hold the piece of cardboard in front of you with the scale facing to the left or right, whichever makes it easier for you to take readings. To take a reading, simply observe where the string crosses the acceleration scale.

2. Stand still and measure your body's acceleration. Record the data in your Science Notebook. Make sure you include the units of measurement with your answer.

3. Find a place where you can walk in a straight line for 10 seconds.

4. Begin walking at a steady pace and measure your acceleration after approximately 5 seconds. Stop walking after you have taken the reading and then record the acceleration you measured.

5. Return to your starting point and stand still again.

6. This time, begin walking, but observe the acceleration as soon as you start walking.

7. Walk forward at a steady pace for approximately 5 seconds and then measure your acceleration as you come to a stop. Record the data in your Science Notebook.

8. Find an area where you can run in a straight line for approximately 100 m.

9. Starting from rest, walk, jog, and then run so the accelerometer reads 1 m/s^2.

10. When you stop, catch your breath and record how long (approximately) you were able to maintain a constant acceleration. Record the data in your Science Notebook.

Questions

1. How is acceleration related to Newton's Second Law of Motion?

    _____

    _____

    _____

    _____

2. What was your acceleration when you were standing still, according to your accelerometer? Be sure to include units in your answer.

    _____

3. What was your acceleration when you were walking at a steady pace, according to your accelerometer? Be sure to include units in your answer.

    _____

4. What did you observe on the accelerometer when you began walking from standing still?

    _____

    _____

Name _____   Date _____

5. What did you observe on the accelerometer as you stopped walking?

   _____

   _____

6. What does your answer in Question 5 tell you about the common misconception that acceleration means speeding up?

   _____

   _____

7. What did you notice when you tried to maintain a constant acceleration of 1 m/s^2 in a straight line?

   _____

   _____

   _____

Student Guide
Lesson 12: Newton's Third Law of Motion

Lesson Objectives

- Explain Newton's Third Law of Motion.
- Interpret diagrams that demonstrate applications of Newton's Third Law.
- Apply Newton's three laws of motion in real-world situations, such as sports activities and transportation.

PREPARE

Approximate lesson time is 60 minutes.

Materials

For the Student

    🖳 Lesson Review

    🖳 Pitcher's Hand

    tennis ball - or rubber ball

    wall, outdoor - brick

LEARN
Activity 1: Newton's Third Law of Motion *(Online)*

Activity 2: Newton's Third Law of Motion *(Online)*

Activity 3: Pitcher's Hand *(Online)*

ASSESS

Lesson Assessment: Newton's Third Law of Motion, Part 1 (*Online*)

You will complete an online assessment covering the main objectives of this lesson. Your assessment will be scored by the computer.

Lesson Assessment: Newton's Third Law of Motion, Part 2 (*Offline*)

You will complete an offline assessment covering the main objectives of this lesson. Your learning coach will score this assessment.

Name _____   Date _____

Newton's Third Law of Motion Review

Use the words from this list to fill in the blanks below. The words may be used more than once and may be used as either singular or plural.

direction

action

magnitude

reaction

backward

pairs

force

Newton's third law deals with force_____ . It states that whenever one object exerts a

_____ on a second object, the second object exerts a force on the first object that is equal in

_____ and opposite in_____ . One force is called the action force and the

other force is called the _____ force. If the masses of the objects are nearly equal, the

first object will move forward and the second object will move_____ .

1. If Paul jumps with a force of −90 N down on a trampoline, what force will the trampoline apply to him?

2. If Paul's mass is 60 kg, how much will he accelerate when the trampoline applies a force of 90 N?

3. If the force of the trampoline moves Paul upward, which direction does the force of Paul's jump move the trampoline?

    _____

Name _____   Date _____

Pitcher's Hand

Materials

rubber ball or tennis ball

sturdy wall outdoors, such as a brick wall at a school playground

Procedure

1. Take a ball and go outdoors. Find a very sturdy wall, such as a brick wall at a school playground. Make sure there are no windows that could accidentally be broken when throwing the ball.

2. Stand about 10 meters from the wall. Toss the ball lightly (and as straight as you can) against the wall and observe.

3. Use a medium amount of force to throw the ball straight against the wall. Move out of the way and observe what happens.

4. Use as much force as you can to throw the ball straight against the wall. Move out of the way again and observe what happens.

5. Repeat Steps 2 through 4, but this time, throw the ball at about a 45-degree angle at the wall. Observe what happens with each throw, light, medium, and hard.

Questions

1. What is the force that causes the ball to hit the wall each time you throw it?

_____

_____

2. What is the force that causes the ball to bounce away from the wall each time you throw it?

_____

_____

3. What happens to the ball each time you increase the force of your throw?

_____

_____

_____

4. What happens when you throw the ball at a 45-degree angle towards the wall?

_____

_____

_____

_____

Name   Date

Newton's Third Law of Motion
Lesson Assessment

Use the following scenario to answer Questions 1–4.

A car traveling at a velocity of 26.6 m/s crashes into a tree. The passenger in the car is wearing a seat belt and is stopped in 2.2 seconds. The mass of the passenger is 50 kg.

1. According the Newton's first law, what will the passenger's motion tend to be during the crash?

    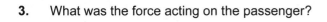

2. Use the formula $a = \Delta v\, /\, \Delta t$ to solve for the acceleration of the passenger.

3. What was the force acting on the passenger?

4. What was the action and reaction force that acted on the seatbelt?

Student Guide
Lesson 13: Buoyant Forces

Lesson Objectives

- Explain that the buoyant force on an object is equal to the weight of the fluid that the object displaces.
- Explain that an object floats when its density is less than the density of the fluid surrounding it.
- Apply the principle of buoyant force to predict whether objects will float or sink in a fluid.

PREPARE

Approximate lesson time is 60 minutes.

Materials

For the Student

- 🖳 Buoyant Forces Review
- 🖳 Float Away

  scale, spring

  tub - plastic or bucket

  bottle, plastic 500 ml

  household items - small objects that can be safely placed in water

  string

  water

Keywords and Pronunciation

Archimedes (ahr-kuh-MEE-deez)

buoyancy (BOY-uhnt-see) : the tendency of an object to float

buoyant force : the upward force on an object which is immersed in a fluid

LEARN
Activity 1: Buoyant Forces *(Online)*

Activity 2: Buoyant Forces *(Online)*

Review what you have learned about buoyant forces. When finished, place your completed lesson review sheet in your Science Notebook.

Activity 3: Float Away (Online)

ASSESS

Lesson Assessment: Buoyant Forces (*Online*)

You will complete an online assessment covering the main objectives of this lesson. Your assessment will be scored by the computer.

Activity 3: Float Away (Online)

Name _____   Date _____

Buoyant Forces Review

Use the words from this list to fill in the blanks in the two paragraphs below. The words may be used more than once and may be used as either singular or plural.

fluid pressure
buoyant force
Archimedes' principle
float
weight
bottom
volume
sink
less dense
smaller

A can of diet soda will_____ and a can of regular soda will_____ when they are put in a tank filled with water. The can of diet soda is _____than the can of regular soda. The can of diet soda has a _____ mass than the can of regular soda. Both cans experience an upward force exerted by the water called_____. The upward force is caused by _____ on the cans. The _____ on the _____ of the can is greater than that on the top.

Buoyant force can be determined by_____ . The _____ of the water displaced by an object equals the_____. An object that is denser than water can float in water if it has a large enough _____ .

Table 1. Fill in the table to indicate if each substance will float or sink.

Data Table 1

Substance	Density (g/mL)	Float or sink in water with a density of 1.00 g/mL
Wood	0.85	
Olive oil	0.92	
Glycerin	1.26	
Bone	1.90	

Table 2. Fill in the table to indicate if each object will float or sink.

Data Table 2

Object	Buoyant Force on Object (N)	Weight of Object (N)	Float or Sink
A	100	200	
B	150	200	
C	200	190	
D	250	200	

Name _____   Date _____

Float Away

Throughout the unit, you have learned about all different types of forces. Water can also act as a force. In the case of liquids, Archimedes' Principle comes into play. Archimedes' Principle states that when an object is immersed in a fluid, there is an upward buoyant force that is equal to the weight of the volume of water displaced by the object. Archimedes' Principle works whether an object floats on the surface of a liquid or sinks.

Materials

plastic tub or bucket (should be at least 15 cm deep)
water
spring scale
bottle, plastic 500ml
string
small plastic container
3-4 small rocks
small household objects of various shapes and weights (that can be placed in water)

Procedure

1. Fill the plastic tub or bucket approximately ¾ full of water.

2. Fill the bottle with water and then hang it on the end of the spring scale. Record its weight in your Science Notebook.

3. Keep the bottle on the spring scale. Submerge the bottle into the water. Do not submerge any part of the scale. Record the weight shown on the spring scale.

4. Tie the small plastic container to the spring scale and repeat Steps 2 and 3.

5. Remove the small plastic container from the water, and place the rocks inside the container. Measure the weight of the container with rocks both in and out of the water.

6. Repeat Steps 2 and 3 with some small household items. If items cannot hang from the spring scale directly, use the string to tie them to the spring scale hook.

7. Use the data you gathered to answer the questions that follow.

Questions

1. How did the measured weight of each object change when you put it in the water?

   _____

   _____

2. What do you think caused this change? Did the actual weight of the object change?

   _____

   _____

   _____

3. What happened when you put the empty plastic container in the water?

   _____

   _____

4. What effect did the rocks have on the plastic container?

   _____

   _____

Student Guide
Lesson 14: Lab: Precious Cargo

Lesson Objectives

- Apply Newton's Laws of Motion in hands-on activities.

PREPARE

Approximate lesson time is 60 minutes.

Materials

For the Student

- ▣ Precious Cargo

  balloons (2)

  cotton balls (10)

  cotton swabs (10)

  cups - plastic foam (2)

  eggs, raw (2)

  ladder - step

  newspaper - or magazines

  tape measure

  tape, masking

  tissues - facial (2)

LEARN
Activity 1: Precious Cargo *(Online)*

ASSESS

Lesson Assessment: Lab: Precious Cargo (*Online*)

Have an adult review your answers to the Lab: Precious Cargo, and input the results online.

Name   Date

Precious Cargo

In this activity, a raw egg will be your passenger, and the plastic foam cups will be your vehicle. You will need to design an interior for the vehicle that will prevent the egg from cracking when the vehicle (with the egg inside) is dropped from a height of 8 feet.

Materials

2 raw eggs

2 plastic foam cups

masking tape

2 balloons

2 facial tissues

10 cotton balls

10 cotton swabs

step ladder

tape measure

newspaper (optional)

Procedure

Making the vehicle:

The shell of your vehicle will be the two plastic foam cups. You will design the interior of your vehicle to protect your egg. After you complete the vehicle's interior, you will put in the egg and use masking tape to seal the two open ends of the vehicle together.

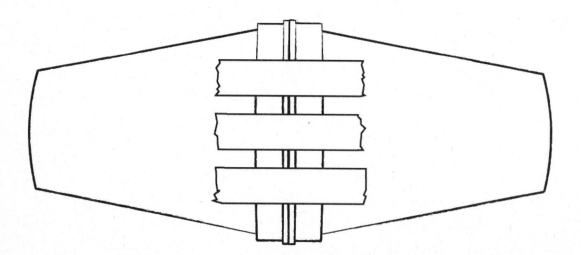

Name _____   Date _____

1. Using any or all of the materials listed above, design the interior of the vehicle that you think will best protect the egg. You cannot use tape directly on the egg (so no wrapping the egg in masking tape). You cannot use any other materials than those listed above. You don't have to use all of the materials.

2. Place the egg inside the vehicle and use the masking tape to seal the vehicle as shown above.

Performing the test:

3. Perform the test outside on concrete or asphalt, if possible. If performing the test inside, be sure to use a hard floor and put down some newspapers in case of a mess. Carefully stand on the step ladder and use the tape measure to measure a height of 8 feet from the ground.

4. With the bottom of your vehicle at the 8-foot mark, let go of the vehicle.

5. Carefully remove the egg from the vehicle.

6. If your egg cracked, get a new egg and try a different design.

7. If your egg did not crack and time permits, change your design so that the vehicle can be dropped sideways without cracking the egg.

Questions

1. Describe the design that worked for you.

_____

_____

_____

_____

2. What forces acted upon the vehicle?

_____

_____

_____

3. What forces acted upon the egg?

_____

_____

_____

4. What do you think would happen if you dropped the vehicle from a height of 16 feet? Why?

_____

_____

_____

_____

Student Guide
Lesson 16: Model Problems

Lesson Objectives

- Gain experience in answering model problems related to topics of the previous lessons.

PREPARE

Approximate lesson time is 60 minutes.

LEARN
Activity 1: Velocity, Speed, and Force *(Online)*

Student Guide
Lesson 17: Unit 4 Review

Lesson Objectives

- Apply Newton's Laws to solve motion-related problems.
- Apply mathematical solutions to solve problems involving speed and velocity of objects.
- Apply Newton's Universal Law of Gravitation to explain how gravity acts upon all objects in the universe.

PREPARE

Approximate lesson time is 60 minutes.

LEARN
Activity 1: Force and Motion *(Online)*

Student Guide
Lesson 18: Unit Assessment

Lesson Objectives

- Apply Newton's Laws to solve motion-related problems.
- Apply mathematical solutions to solve problems involving speed and velocity of objects.
- Apply Newton's Universal Law of Gravitation to explain how gravity acts upon all objects in the universe.

PREPARE

Approximate lesson time is 60 minutes.

ASSESS

Unit Assessment: Force and Motion, Part 1 (*Online*)

You will complete an online assessment of the main objectives covered so far in this unit. Follow the instructions online. Your assessment will be scored by the computer.

Unit Assessment: Force and Motion, Part 2 (*Offline*)

Complete the offline part of the Unit Assessment. Your learning coach will score this part of the Assessment.

Student Guide
Lesson 1: Semester 1 Review

You've learned a lot over the past few months. Some of the topics you've studied during the first semester include:

1. An Introduction to Physical
   Science
2. Properties of Matter
3. Atoms and Molecules
4. Chemistry
5. Force and Motion

Let's review what you've learned before you take the Semester Assessment.

You're only halfway through the year, but you've covered a lot of material. You'll be taking the Semester Assessment soon, so let's review topics you've studied so far.

Lesson Objectives

- Apply Newton's Laws to solve motion-related problems.
- Describe how scientists use models to represent and predict real phenomena in the physical world.
- Make measurements using the SI system.
- Describe the structure of an atom, of an element, and its isotopes.
- Describe the patterns of organization represented in the periodic table.
- Explain how the motion of molecules differs in different states of matter.
- Compare the chemistry of ionic and covalent bonds.
- Balance chemical equations and explain what it means to balance such an equation.
- Explain that energy is always involved in chemical reactions either as absorption of heat (endothermic) or release of heat (exothermic).

PREPARE

Approximate lesson time is 60 minutes.

Materials

For the Student

⌨ Semester 1 Review

LEARN
Activity 1: Semester 1 Review (Online)

This review lesson represents many of the topics you've studied so far this year. First, print out the Semester 1 Review worksheet. Follow the directions to locate information from the first semester units. Make sure you have your Science Notebook handy. When you have completed the activity, you will be ready to take the Semester Assessment.

Name _____   Date _____

Semester Review

Section 1: Measuring Matter

During this semester, you learned about an international system of units that scientists use to describe measurements of matter. This system is called the International System of Units (SI).

1. Explain why this system was developed.

    _____

    _____

2. Imagine you conducted a scientific experiment in the lab and you want another scientist to repeat it. What SI unit would you use to describe the mass of chemicals used in the experiment?

    _____

3. What SI unit would you use to describe temperature in this experiment?

    _____

4. If you write these directions for an experiment, why would someone else have a problem following them? "Hold the chemicals 1.5 feet above the heat source."

    _____

    _____

Hint: You can find the answers to this section's questions in Lesson 3 of Unit 1.

Section 2: Atoms and Matter

All matter is made of atoms. You may remember that atoms are made up of particles called protons, neutrons, and electrons. Protons and neutrons are present in the nucleus of an atom. Electrons circle the atom's nucleus in atomic shells.

5. Complete the following chart to show the charge of each particle in an atom.

Particle	Charge
Proton	
Neutron	
Electron	

Use this model of a lithium atom to answer Questions 6 and 7.

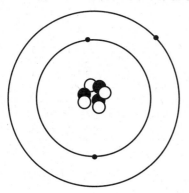

3 protons (solid circles)
4 neutrons (open circles)
3 electrons (small solid circles)

6. How is the model like a real atom? How is the model different from a real atom?

_____

_____

7. The atomic number of an atom is equal to the number of protons in its nucleus. The atomic mass of an atom is (approximately) equal to the sum of its protons and neutrons. Look at the above illustration and determine the atomic number and atomic mass of a lithium atom. Remember that the number of electrons in an atom is equal to the number of protons.

_____

Hint: If you are unsure how to answer the questions from Section 2, you can look up the information in Lesson 1 of Unit 2.

Section 3: Elements and Isotopes

Each atom of a specific element has the same number of protons. But, the number of neutrons may be different. Atoms of the same element with a different number of neutrons are called isotopes.

8. An element is made up of matter that includes only one type of atom. Suppose you have a sample of an element. What is the smallest portion of that element that has all the properties of the element?

    _____

9. We name isotopes by using the name of the atom and its total number of protons and neutrons. A carbon atom with six protons and six neutrons is called carbon-12. How many protons and neutrons are in an atom of carbon-14? Explain how you know.

    _____

    _____

Hint: If you have trouble answering these questions, you can review atoms and isotopes in Lessons 1 and 2 of Unit 2.

Section 4: The Periodic Table

Several scientists designed periodic tables, but the Russian chemist, Dmitri Mendeleev, was the first to get it essentially right. Mendeleev's table looks much like the one scientists use today. Review the Periodic Table of Elements shown below, then use the table to answer Question 10.

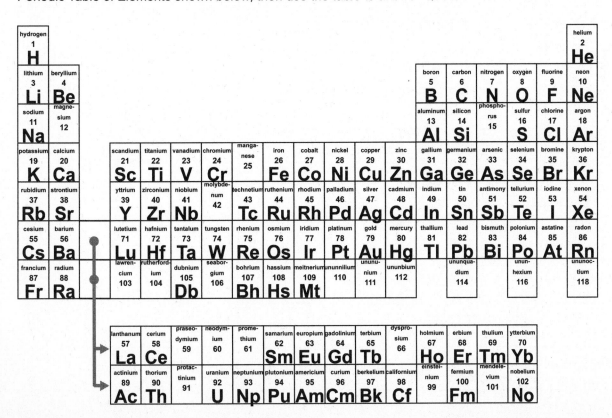

10. How do the elements change as you go from left to right across a row (period)?

_____

_____

_____

11. What is common to all the elements in a group?

_____

12. Which two elements in the periodic table are more alike — oxygen (O) and sulfur (S) OR sulfur (S) and chlorine (Cl)? Explain your answer.

_____

_____

13. Elements in the periodic table are also organized into families. Families of elements share some properties. Can you name three families in the periodic table?

_____

Hint: If you have trouble answering these questions, you can go to Lessons 3 and 4 of Unit 2 and review the basics of the periodic table.

Section 5: Covalent and Ionic Bonding

Remember that a molecule is formed by the chemical bonding of two or more atoms. Two types of chemical bonds are ionic bonds and covalent bonds.

14. Complete the table by placing a checkmark in the correct box.

	Covalent Bond	Ionic Bond
Bond is formed by the attraction of ions with opposite charges		
Bond is formed when two atoms share an electron		
Result of bonding is a molecule		
Result of bonding is an ionic compound		
Electrons are transferred from one atom to another		

15. How many electrons do most atoms need in their outer shell (valence electrons) to remain stable?

_____

16. If there is only one electron in the outer shell of an atom, what is the one way for it to become stable?

_____

_____

_____

Hint: If you have trouble completing this section, you can look up the information in Unit 3.

Section 6: Molecular Motion in States of Matter

Do you remember what you learned about the motion of molecules in solids, liquids, and gases? To help you review, let's take a closer look at how molecules move.

17. How does the movement of molecules differ when matter changes from a solid to a liquid?

_____

_____

_____

_____

18. What is the relationship between the temperature of matter and molecular movement?

_____

Hint: If you are unsure how to answer the questions in this section, you can look up the information in Lesson 7 of Unit 2.

Section 7: Chemical Equations

19. When atoms of different elements are combined, they can form compounds. The chemical reactions that create these substances will produce heat or absorb heat. What are the terms for these two types of chemical reactions?

   _____

When an acid and a base react, they form a salt and water in a neutralization reaction. Scientists use chemical equations to represent these chemical reactions. Here is the chemical equation for the neutralization of hydrochloric acid (HCl) and potassium hydroxide (KOH):

$$HCl^+ + KOH^- \rightarrow KCl + H_2O$$

   acid   base   salt water

20. What is the law of conservation of mass and how is it represented in the above equation?

   _____

   _____

   _____

Hint: If you have trouble answering the questions in this section, review the lessons from Unit 3.

Section 8: Force and Motion

During this semester, you learned about Newton's Universal Law of Gravitation and Newton's three Laws of Motion. Let's review what you have learned.

21. Alicia is riding her bicycle in a straight line on level pavement. Suddenly, her front bicycle tire hits a rock, and she goes flying over the front handlebars. Explain why Alicia went flying over the front handlebars. Refer to one of Newton's Laws of Motion in your explanation.

   _____

   _____

   _____

   _____

   _____

22. Now, imagine that Alicia is a passenger in the front seat of a car. She is wearing her seat belt and the car is traveling on a highway. Suddenly, the driver sees a dog run into the road, so he slams on the brakes. What will happen to Alicia this time? How does this illustrate Newton's Laws of Motion?

_____

_____

_____

_____

23. This time, think of Alicia as an astronaut. She is inside the space shuttle on the launch pad, waiting for take-off. With a huge burst of energy, the rocket engines roar, and the shuttle soars upward. Apply Newton's Laws of motion to explain how the rocket engines work to get the shuttle going.

_____

_____

_____

_____

Hint: If you have trouble answering the questions in this section, review the lessons from Unit 4.

Section 9: More Force and Motion

According to Newton's Second Law of Motion, the relationship among force (_F_), mass (_m_), and acceleration (_a_) is _F = ma_.

24. Newton's Second Law of Motion explains how force, mass, and acceleration are related. Here is the formula, Force = mass x acceleration. Suppose your family has a new car which accelerates at 2 m/sec/sec ($2 m/s^2$). If the car's mass is measured as 1500 kg, how much force (in newtons) will be required to get the car moving?

_____

_____

25. For a larger vehicle, like a truck, explain the difference in force required to get the truck moving.

_____

_____

Hint: If you have trouble answering the questions in this section, review the lessons from Unit 4.

Student Guide
Lesson 2: Semester 1 Assessment

During the first semester you've studied many different topics: the SI measurement system, properties of matter, atoms and molecules, chemistry and equations, and force and motion. It is now time to take the Semester Assessment to test your understanding of these concepts. Before you start, print a copy of the Periodic Table of Elements.

Lesson Objectives

- Distinguish between a closed system and an open system.
- Apply Newton's Laws to solve motion-related problems.
- Describe how scientists use models to represent and predict real phenomena in the physical world.
- Make measurements using the SI system.
- Describe the structure of an atom, of an element, and its isotopes.
- Describe the patterns of organization represented in the periodic table.
- Explain how the motion of molecules differs in different states of matter.
- Compare the chemistry of ionic and covalent bonds.
- Balance chemical equations and explain what it means to balance such an equation.
- Explain that energy is always involved in chemical reactions either as absorption of heat (endothermic) or release of heat (exothermic).

PREPARE

Approximate lesson time is 60 minutes.

ASSESS

Semester Assessment: Physical Science, Semester 1, Part 1 (*Online*)

You will complete an assessment covering the main objectives of this semester. This part of the assessment is online. It will be scored by the computer.

Semester Assessment: Physical Science, Semester 1, Part 2 (*Offline*)

Complete the offline part of the Semester Assessment. Your learning coach will score this part of the assessment.

Periodic Table of Elements

hydrogen 1 H 1.01																	helium 2 He 4.00
lithium 3 Li 6.94	beryllium 4 Be 9.01											boron 5 B 10.81	carbon 6 C 12.01	nitrogen 7 N 14.01	oxygen 8 O 15.99	fluorine 9 F 18.99	neon 10 Ne 20.18
sodium 11 Na 22.99	magnesium 12 Mg 24.31											aluminum 13 Al 26.98	silicon 14 Si 28.09	phosphorus 15 P 30.97	sulfur 16 S 32.07	chlorine 17 Cl 35.45	argon 18 Ar 39.95
potassium 19 K 39.10	calcium 20 Ca 40.08	scandium 21 Sc 44.96	titanium 22 Ti 47.87	vanadium 23 V 50.94	chromium 24 Cr 51.99	manganese 25 Mn 54.94	iron 26 Fe 55.85	cobalt 27 Co 58.93	nickel 28 Ni 58.69	copper 29 Cu 63.55	zinc 30 Zn 65.41	gallium 31 Ga 69.72	germanium 32 Ge 72.64	arsenic 33 As 74.92	selenium 34 Se 78.96	bromine 35 Br 79.91	krypton 36 Kr 83.80
rubidium 37 Rb 82.47	strontium 38 Sr 87.62	yttrium 39 Y 88.91	zirconium 40 Zr 91.22	niobium 41 Nb 92.91	molybdenum 42 Mo 95.94	technetium 43 Tc 98	ruthenium 44 Ru 101.07	rhodium 45 Rh 102.91	palladium 46 Pd 106.42	silver 47 Ag 107.87	cadmium 48 Cd 112.41	indium 49 In 114.82	tin 50 Sn 118.71	antimony 51 Sb 121.76	tellurium 52 Te 127.6	iodine 53 I 126.90	xenon 54 Xe 131.29
cesium 55 Cs 132.91	barium 56 Ba 137.34	lutetium 71 Lu 174.97	hafnium 72 Hf 178.49	tantalum 73 Ta 180.94	tungsten 74 W 183.84	rhenium 75 Re 186.21	osmium 76 Os 190.23	iridium 77 Ir 192.22	platinum 78 Pt 195.08	gold 79 Au 196.97	mercury 80 Hg 200.59	thallium 81 Tl 204.38	lead 82 Pb 207.19	bismuth 83 Bi 208.98	polonium 84 Po 209	astatine 85 At 210	radon 86 Rn 222
francium 87 Fr 223	radium 88 Ra 226.03	lawrencium 103 Lr 262	rutherfordium 104 Rf 261	dubnium 105 Db 262	seaborgium 106 Sg 266	bohrium 107 Bh 264	hassium 108 Hs 269	meitnerium 109 Mt 268	ununnilium 110 Uun 271	unununium 111 Uuu 272	ununbium 112 Uub 285		ununquadium 114 Uuq 289		ununhexium 116 Uuh ?		ununoctium 118 Uuo ?

lanthanum 57 La 138.91	cerium 58 Ce 140.11	praseodymium 59 Pr 140.91	neodymium 60 Nd 144.24	promethium 61 Pm 146.92	samarium 62 Sm 150.36	europium 63 Eu 151.96	gadolinium 64 Gd 157.25	terbium 65 Tb 158.92	dysprosium 66 Dy 162.50	holmium 67 Ho 164.93	erbium 68 Er 167.26	thulium 69 Tm 168.93	ytterbium 70 Yb 173.04
actinium 89 Ac 227	thorium 90 Th 232.04	protactinium 91 Pa 231.04	uranium 92 U 238.03	neptunium 93 Np 237	plutonium 94 Pu 244	americium 95 Am 243	curium 96 Cm 247	berkelium 97 Bk 247	californium 98 Cf 251	einsteinium 99 Es 252	fermium 100 Fm 257	mendelevium 101 Md 258	nobelium 102 No 259